Handling data

ENTRY LEVEL 3

Jayne Garner
Joy Collins

ISBN 978-1-84618-163-4

Axis Education, PO Box 459
Shrewsbury SY4 4WZ.
email: enquiries@axiseducation.co.uk
www.axiseducation.co.uk

First published September 2003
Second edition (revised and reset) 2006
Third edition 2008

Contents

Introduction

Functional Skillbuilders have been specifically developed to support teachers delivering Functional Skills and the Skills for Life framework in Adult Literacy and Numeracy. There are 32 volumes in the series providing a dedicated Functional Skillbuilder volume for each section and level of the Functional Skills standards/Adult Literacy and Numeracy Curricula. There are 2 IT volumes at Levels 1 and 2.

All the task-based activities in Functional Skillbuilders are based in three workplace settings – a hotel, a supermarket and a factory. This helps make the activities both real and relevant to adult and young adult learners. Knowledge about each workplace builds cumulatively as students progress through the levels. The tasks become increasingly work specific as students progress through the series. At Entry Level 3 Handling Data tasks remain straightforward, but become increasingly work focused.

Functional Skills

These activities are task-based and provide teachers with a variety of materials to build the full range of Functional Maths skills relating to handling data. The first section of the book explicitly teaches the functional handling data skills required at Entry Level 3. Students then have 2–3 more opportunities to build and apply these skills in vocational contexts, allowing the teacher to teach skills, enable practise and to check learning. At Entry Level 3 students are expected to check the accuracy of their calculations and results. You should encourage them to do this by getting them to add numbers in a different order, using inverse calculations and by estimating answers by rounding.

Functional Skillbuilders are designed to be mediated by teachers. The teaching notes explain the skills addressed on each worksheet and provide guidance for teaching strategies. Teaching materials have also been included. Overhead transparency templates for group work are included at every level.

How to use this pack

Ask the student to complete the checklist on page xi with you. This checklist will tell you the handling data skills your student most wants to practise. Use the outcome of this discussion to agree targets with the student and use the table to identify suitable worksheets.

Teaching notes

There are teaching notes for each worksheet. They explain the purpose of each worksheet and any groundwork that the teacher needs to cover first. The teaching notes include suggestions for group work, work in pairs and extension work.

Introduction

Worksheets

A box like this at the top of each worksheet tells students the skills they will practise, ensuring that they are aware of learning outcomes from the outset.

Teaching point

If there are any teaching points on the worksheet they will appear like this.

Tutor questions

tutor questions

Questions to be read aloud by the teacher appear at the bottom of the worksheet in a box like this.

Curriculum elements matrix

For ready reference by the teacher, a matrix of adult core curriculum elements mapped to all the worksheets is provided on page 64. Mapping to the Functional Skills standards is available electronically. Please email enquiries@axiseducation.co.uk.

Additional teaching materials

Overhead transparency templates for group work are at the very back of the pack. Photocopy them on acetate as required.

These teaching notes are organised by worksheet. There are teaching notes for every worksheet and they are designed to be read in conjunction with a photocopy of the relevant worksheet. The skills covered map to the **Student checklist** on page xi of this pack. The Groundwork section highlights the skills that need to be taught before your students tackle the worksheets, together with teaching suggestions. Paired and group work suggestions are also included.

Worksheet 1
Understand ways of presenting data

Groundwork

This worksheet serves as an introduction to the methods of presenting data expected at Entry Level 3. You should discuss each method and explain how different methods suit different sets of data.

Worksheet

Read through the information on the worksheet with your students and ask them to carry out the task.

Worksheets 2, 3
Understand that chart titles, labels and keys provide vital information. Label a bar chart

Groundwork

Use the teaching point to help explain that data presented in charts must be clearly labelled to convey information effectively.

Worksheets

Explain the skills your students are going to practise, then read the instructions to them.

Group work

Overhead transparency (OHT) templates 1 and 2 provide students with further opportunities to label charts. Use the OHTs to conduct these exercises as group activities.

OHT 1 data:
Modes of transport by Old Hall Hotel workers to get to work in July 2008
Modes of transport, numbers of staff
walk 7, cycle 12, motorbike 8, car 49, bus 31, share lift 19.

OHT 2 data:
UK imports of bananas 1992 and 1998 by principal countries
Countries, numbers of bananas
Costa Rica 10,000 82,000, Dominica 42,000 24,000, France 42,000 135,000, Honduras 10,000 42,000, Jamaica 75,000 62,000
Other EU 98,000 182,000, St Lucia 130,000 70,000

Extension work

Source a selection of straightforward tables and charts. Remove the titles and ask students to suggest suitable titles. Carry out a similar task and this time remove the title of one or both axes.

Worksheets 4, 5, 16, 28, 40
Use a scale

Groundwork

Use the teaching point on Worksheet 4 to explain what a scale is and how to find it on a chart, map or diagram. If possible, bring a selection of charts, maps and diagrams to class and ask students to identify the scale.

Worksheets

Explain the skills your students are going to practise, then ask them to carry out the tasks. These worksheets are similar activities requiring students to use a scale contextualised to the hotel, supermarket and factory. You could use Worksheets 4 and 5 to *teach*, Worksheets 16 and 28 to *reinforce* and Worksheet 40 to *check* your students' ability to use a scale.

Group work

OHT template 3 provides students with a further opportunity to use a scale. Use the OHT to conduct this exercise as a group activity.

Extension work

Source a selection of charts, maps and diagrams with scales and use them as the basis of a variety of activities:

- identify the scale
- calculate real sizes/distances
- ask students to reproduce the data using a different scale.

Worksheets 6, 7
Compare information in bar charts

Groundwork

Use the teaching point to explain how to compare information from bar charts. Make sure that your students understand the terms *axis*, *column* and *title*.

Worksheets

Explain the skills your students are going to practise, then ask them to carry out the tasks.

Group work

OHT template 4 provides students with a further opportunity to extract information from a bar chart. Use the OHT to conduct this exercise as a group activity.

Worksheets 8, 9, 23, 31
Compare and extract information in pictograms

Groundwork

Use the teaching point to explain how to extract information from a pictogram. Make sure that your students understand that the icon can represent more than one of something.

Worksheets

Explain the skills your students are going to practise, then read the instructions to them. These worksheets are similar activities requiring students to extract information from pictograms contextualised to the hotel and supermarket. You could use Worksheets 8 and 9 to *teach*, Worksheet 23 to *reinforce* and Worksheets 31 to *check* your students' ability to extract information from pictograms.

Group work

OHT template 5 provides students with a further opportunity to extract information from a pictogram. Use the OHT to conduct this exercise as a group activity.

Worksheets 10, 11, 17, 18, 20, 21, 24, 29, 30, 32, 33, 41, 43, 47, 50
Compare and extract information in tables

Groundwork

Use the teaching point to explain how to extract information from tables. Make sure that your students understand the terms *row* and *column*.

Worksheets

Explain the skills your students are going to practise, then read the instructions to them. These worksheets are similar activities requiring students to extract information from tables contextualised to the hotel, supermarket and factory. You could use a selection of worksheets to *teach*, a selection of worksheets to *reinforce* and a selection of worksheets to *check* your students' ability to extract information from tables.

Group work

OHT template 6 provides students with a further opportunity to extract information from a table. Use the OHT to conduct this exercise as a group activity.

Extension work

Source a selection of straightforward tables and lists. Use the tables as source material for extracting information.

Worksheets 12, 13, 25, 27, 35, 38, 39, 42, 44, 46, 49
Use a tally chart. Collect data

Groundwork

Use the teaching point on Worksheet 12 to explain how to count tally marks.

Worksheets

Explain the skills your students are going to practise, then ask them to carry out the tasks. These worksheets are similar activities requiring students to use a tally chart contextualised to the hotel, supermarket and factory. You could use a selection of worksheets to *teach*, a selection of worksheets to *reinforce* and a selection of worksheets to *check* your students' ability to use a tally chart and collect data.

Extension work

Ask students to gather and present information on topics of their own choice. Help them to formulate clear questions before going ahead with their data collection using a tally chart.

Worksheets 14, 15
Understand simple pie charts

Groundwork

Use the teaching points on the worksheets to explain how pie charts work. You should introduce the terms title and key.

Worksheets

Explain the skills your students are going to practise, then ask them to carry out the tasks.

Extension work

Source a selection of simple pie charts (no more than four segments) and use them as the basis of a variety of activities similar to those on worksheets 14 and 15.

Worksheets 16, 28, 40
Extract information from a map

Worksheets

Explain the skills your students are going to practise, then ask them to carry out the tasks. These worksheets are similar activities requiring students to use a map contextualised to the hotel, supermarket and factory. You could use a Worksheet 16 to *teach*, Worksheet 28 to *reinforce* and Worksheet 40 to *check* your students' ability to extract information from a map.

Group work

OHT template 3 provides students with a further opportunity to use a map. Use the OHT to conduct this exercise as a group activity.

Extension work

Source a selection of maps and use them as the basis of a variety of activities:

- calculate journey distances
- estimate journey times
- work out the quickest route from one destination to another
- use a mileage chart.

Worksheets 17, 18, 21, 22, 25, 27, 29, 33, 34, 35, 36, 37, 38, 39, 41, 43, 44, 45, 47, 48, 49 Construct bar charts

Groundwork

Remind your students about the need to present data clearly. They will need to decide which way to present the axes. Re-use Worksheets 2 and 3 if necessary.

Worksheets

Ask students to construct bar charts using the data provided. These worksheets are similar activities requiring students to construct bar charts contextualised to the hotel, supermarket and factory. You could use a selection of worksheets to *teach*, a selection of worksheets to *reinforce* and a selection of worksheets to *check* your students' ability to construct bar charts.

Worksheets 19, 25, 26, 35, 36, 44, 46 Compare and extract information in lists

Worksheets

Explain the skills your students are going to practise, then read the instructions to them. These worksheets are similar activities requiring students to extract information from tables contextualised to the hotel, supermarket and factory. You could use Worksheets 19 and 25 to *teach*, Worksheets 26, 35, 36 to *reinforce* and Worksheets 44, 46 to *check* your students' ability to extract information from lists.

Extension work

Source a selection of straightforward lists. Use the lists as source material for extracting information.

Worksheets 19, 22, 27, 30, 38, 39, 43, 49 Construct pictograms

Groundwork

Remind your students about the need to present data clearly. They will need to decide which way to present the axes. Re-use Worksheets 8 and 9 if you feel your students need a re-cap on pictograms.

Worksheets

Ask students to construct pictograms using the data provided. These worksheets are similar activities requiring students to construct pictograms contextualised to the hotel, supermarket and factory. You could use a selection of worksheets to *teach*, a selection of worksheets to *reinforce* and a selection of worksheets to *check* your students' ability to construct pictograms.

Worksheets 22, 23, 27, 31, 32, 33, 34, 38, 45
Present data in a table

Groundwork

Remind your students about the need to present data clearly. Re-use Worksheets 10 and 11 if you feel your students need a re-cap on tables.

Worksheets

Ask students to complete the tables using the data provided. These worksheets are similar activities requiring students to present data in a table contextualised to the hotel, supermarket and factory. You could use a selection of worksheets to *teach*, a selection of worksheets to *reinforce* and a selection of worksheets to *check* your students' ability to present data in a table.

Student checklist

Functional Skillbuilders Handling Data Entry Level 3 will help you improve your Fuctional Maths skills. This chart lists the data handling skills covered in this book. Tick the boxes to say which skills you think you will find the most useful to practise. Then discuss your ideas with your teacher.

Skill	✔	Worksheets
Carry out a survey		9, 26, 34, 35, 37, 39
Construct a block graph		17, 18, 19, 21, 24, 26, 31, 32, 34, 35, 39, 51
Count tally marks		20, 23, 31, 32, 33, 46, 51
Extract data from lists		28, 29, 40, 45, 52
Extract data from price lists		37, 46, 48, 49
Extract data from block graphs/bar charts		4, 5, 16, 25, 27, 35, 47, 50
Extract data from pictograms		34, 35
Extract data from tables		2, 3, 19, 23, 24, 25, 27, 38, 43, 44, 51
Give a block graph a title		13
Label axes on a block graph		12
Present data in a pictogram		23, 33, 38, 44
Present data in a table		26, 34, 35, 37, 39, 45
Present data in a timetable		20, 30, 42
Sort and classify objects using two criteria		6, 7, 28, 29, 40, 41, 52, 53
Understand different ways to present data		1, 10, 11
Understand pie charts		14, 15
Use a tally chart to collect data		8, 9, 20, 23,31

Understand ways of presenting data.

There is a range of different ways of presenting data. You could use any of the following:

- list
- table
- pictogram
- block graph (also known as a bar chart)
- diagram.

Use arrows to match the method of presentation to the correct title.

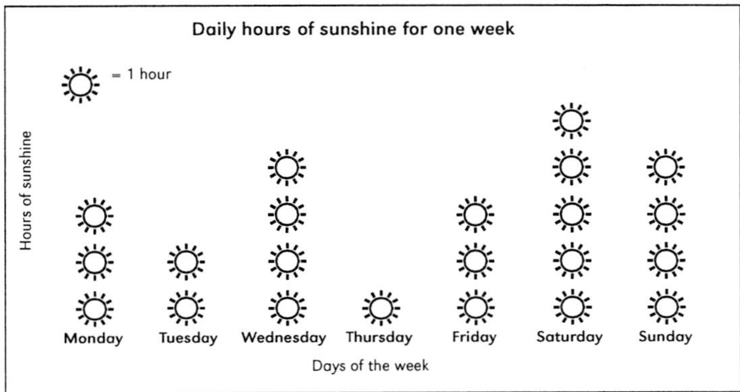

Trouser press instructions

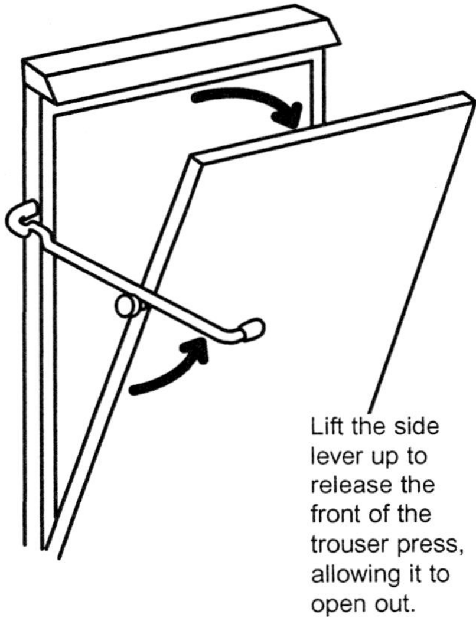

Birthday list

1. Dad 1st January
2. Ken 3rd February
3. Ann 22nd April
4. Nan 4th June
5. Bill 7th July
6. Mum 18th July

List

Table

Pictogram

Block graph

Diagram

Music sales

	CDs	Tapes
Pop	20	3
Country and western	15	1
Classical	5	1
Heavy metal	8	2

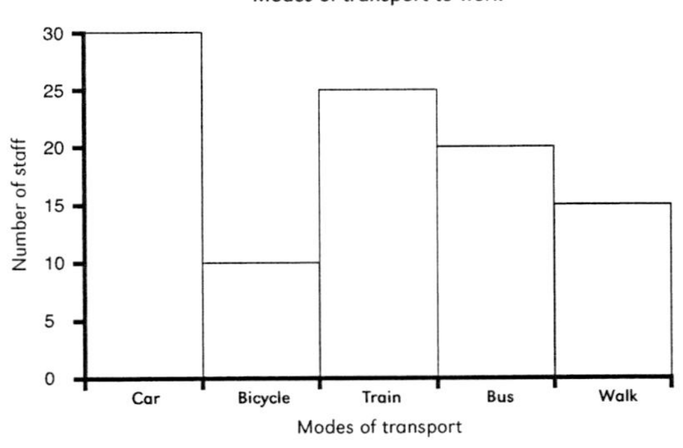

2. Labelling data 1

Understand that chart titles, labels and keys provide data.

The purpose of presenting data is to convey information. Titles, labels and sometimes a key are important when reading and gaining information from charts.

Look at the data on Worksheet 1 and answer these questions.

1. What is the title of the table? ______
2. What is the title of the block graph? ______
3. What is the title of the pictogram? ______
4. What is the title of the diagram? ______
5. What are the labels on the table? ______
6. What are the labels on the pictogram? ______
7. What do the labels on the bar chart tell you? ______
8. What information does the key on the pictogram give you? ______
9. Would a key be useful on any of the other data? If so, say what the key should include.

______

______

The bar chart on Worksheet 3 hasn't got a title, labels or a key. Use the text below to fill in the blanks.

Percentage of staff
Drinks
Lemonade (10% and 7%)
Fizzy water (15% and 27%)
Hot chocolate (20% and 7%)
Tea (25% and 39%)
Coffee (30% and 20%)
Mid-morning drink preferences of housekeeping and leisure club staff
Housekeeping staff (white)
Leisure club staff (grey)

3. Labelling data 2

Label a bar chart.

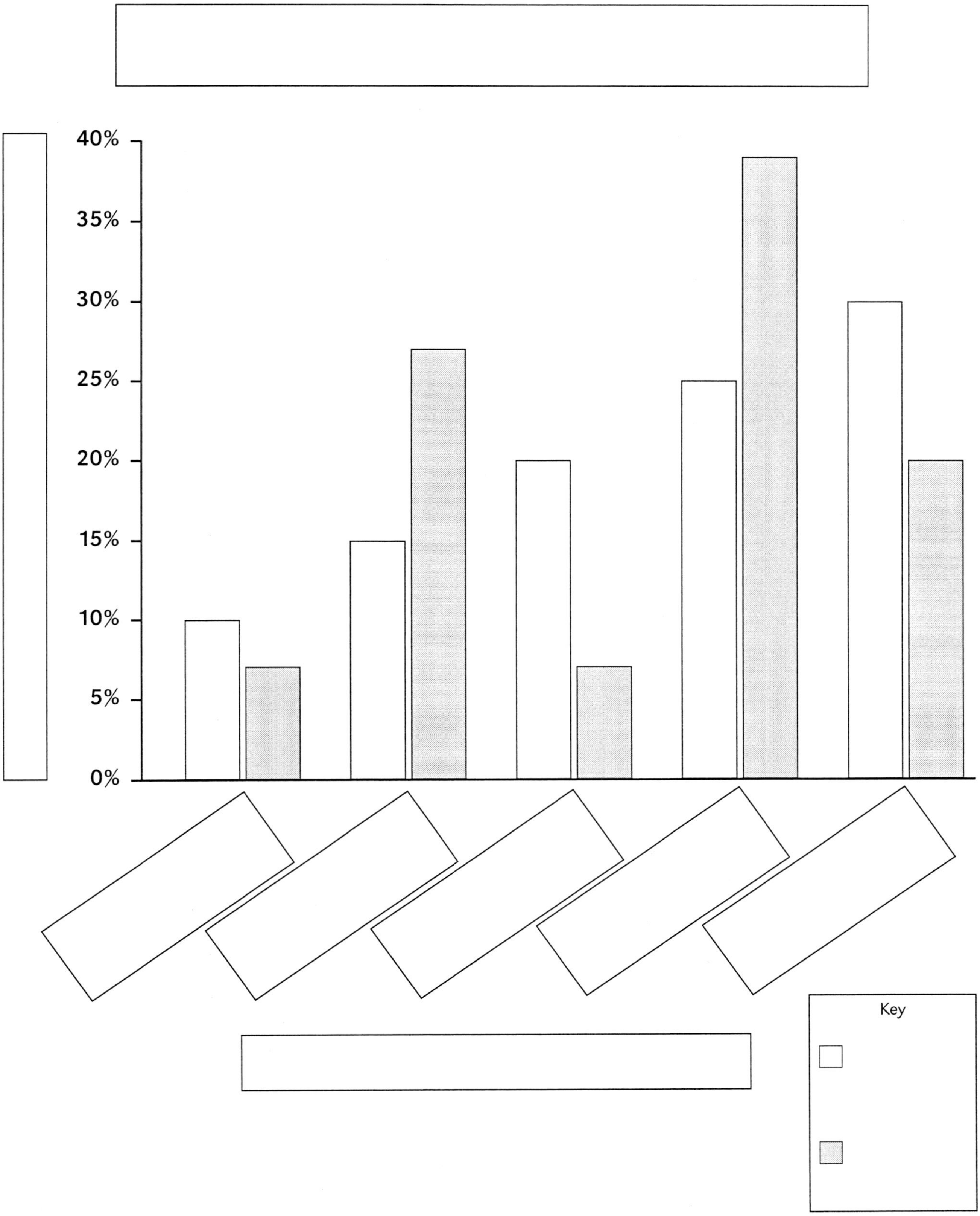

4. Using scale 1

Use a scale to extract numerical values.

Many methods of representing data use a *scale*. Scale is the relation between the real size of something and its size on a map, model or diagram. You might see or hear these expressions:

- *A scale of 1:20,000.*
- *She was making a scale model of a battleship.*
- *This is a large-scale diagram.* (meaning that things are shown in detail).
- *The house is shown to scale.* (meaning that the exact shape of the house is shown, but much smaller)

If a scale has been used, it should be written on the chart or diagram

When you get information from a diagram using a scale, you have to work out the ratio of the actual measurement to the real measurement.

Look at these diagrams. What is the scale of each one? Write your answers in the boxes.

1

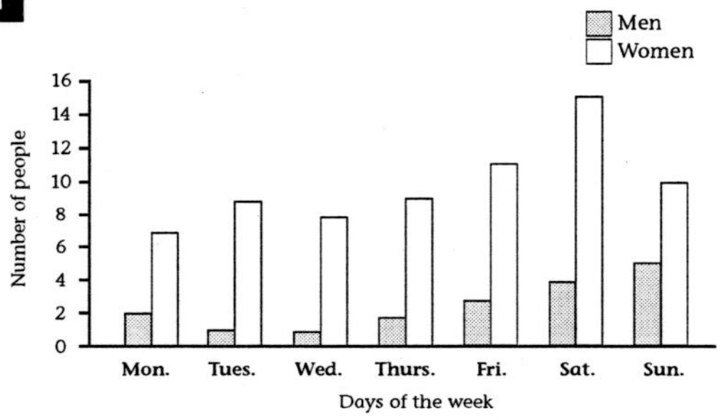

Men
Women
Number of people
0 2 4 6 8 10 12 14 16
Mon. Tues. Wed. Thurs. Fri. Sat. Sun.
Days of the week

2

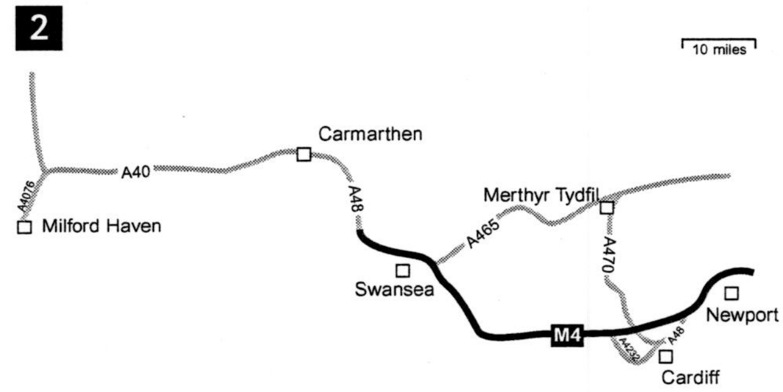

10 miles
Carmarthen
A40
A4076
Milford Haven
A48
Merthyr Tydfil
A465
A470
Swansea
M4
Newport
A4232
A48
Cardiff

3

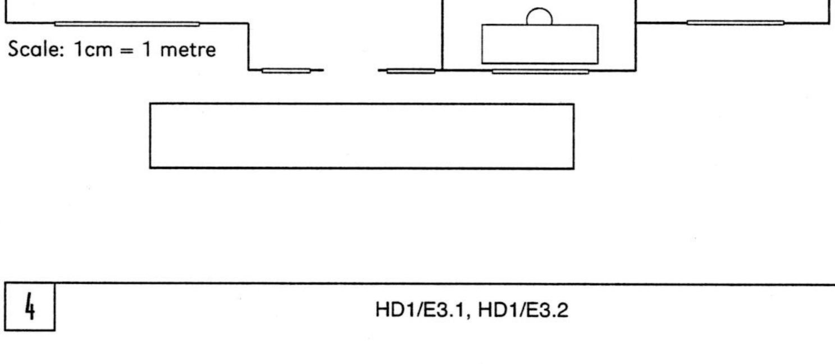

Utility
Kitchen
Cloakroom
Dining room
Living room
Hall
Study
Scale: 1cm = 1 metre

4

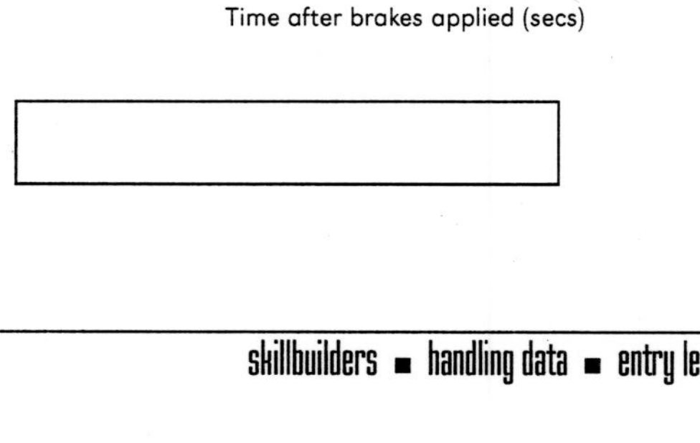

Speed (mph)
10 20 30 40 50 60
0 2 4 6 8 10
Time after brakes applied (secs)

Use a scale to extract numerical values.

This diagram of a room is drawn to the scale of 1cm = 1m. Use this information to answer the questions.

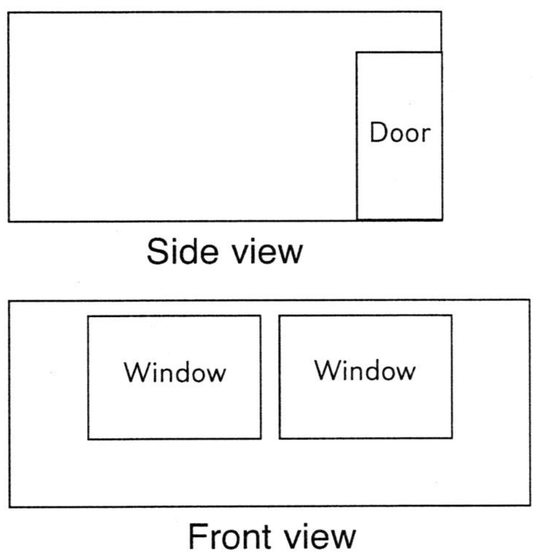

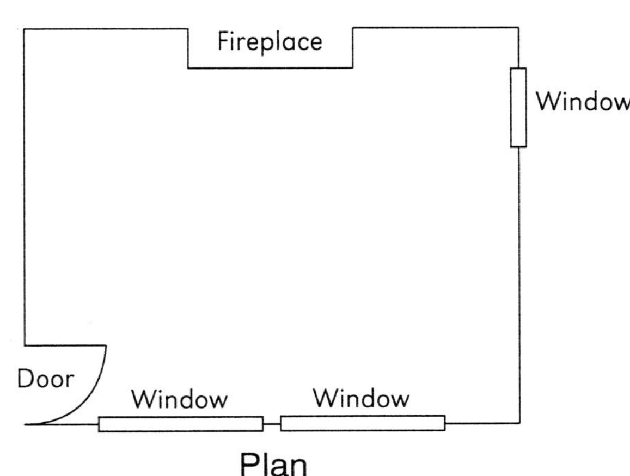

1. How high are the walls? Give your answer in metres.
2. How wide is the wall with the fireplace? Give your answer in metres.
3. How wide is the wall with one window? Give your answer in metres.
4. How wide is the wall with two windows? Give your answer in metres.
5. How wide is the wall with the door? Give your answer in metres.
6. How high is the door? Give your answer in centimetres.
7. How wide is the door? Give your answer in centimetres.
8. How high are the front windows? Give your answer in centimetres.
9. How wide are the front windows? Give your answer in centimetres.
10. How wide is the fireplace? Give your answer in centimetres.
11. Work out the perimeter of the room. Give your answer in metres.

6. Extract information from bar charts 1

Compare information in bar charts.

Numerical information in bar charts can be presented in two ways.
The height of the bars can be compared, as in this example:

Mid-morning drink preferences of housekeeping and leisure club staff

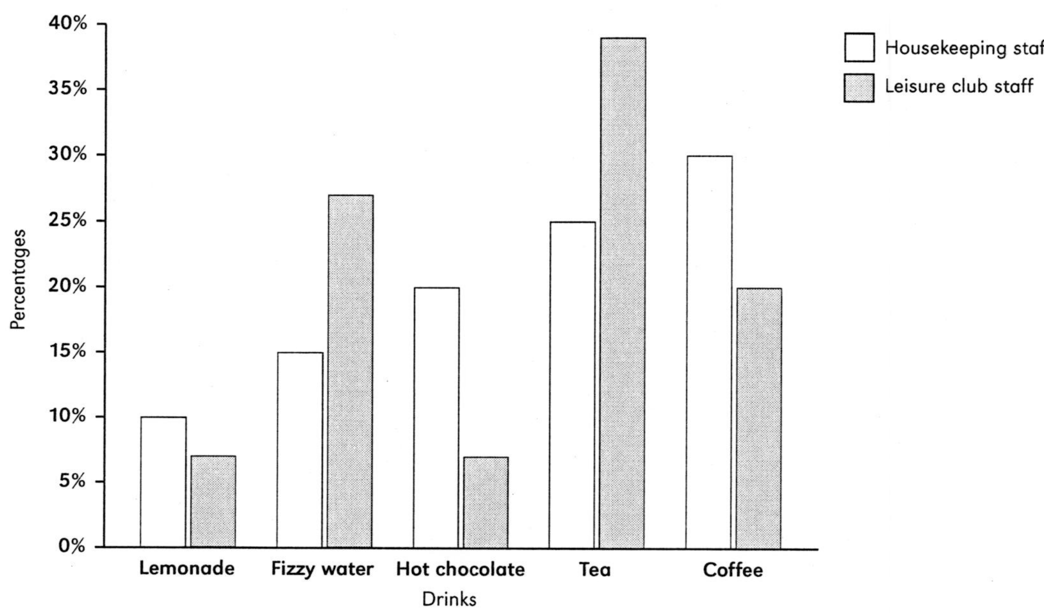

Or the length of the bars can be compared, as in this example:

Mid-morning drink preferences of housekeeping and leisure club staff

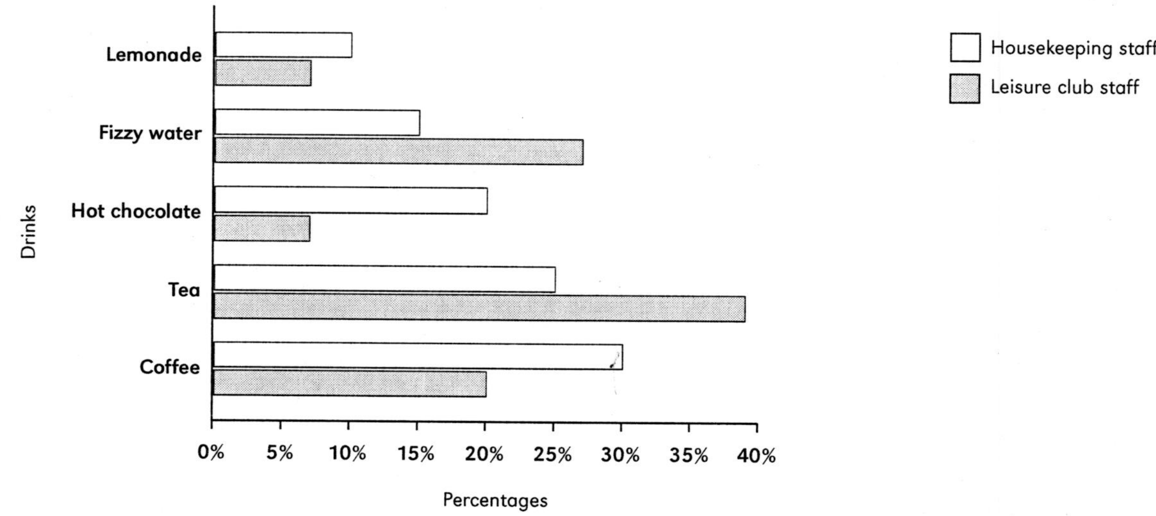

7. Extract information from bar charts 2

skillbuild

Compare information in bar charts.

Use the information in the first bar chart on Worksheet 6, comparing the height of the bars, to answer these questions.

1. What percentage of leisure club staff preferred to drink tea? __________

2 What percentage of leisure club staff preferred cold drinks? __________

3. What was the most popular drink amongst leisure club staff? __________

4. What was the least popular drink amongst leisure club staff? __________

5. What was the most popular drink overall? __________

6. What percentage of housekeeping staff preferred lemonade? __________

Use the information in the second bar chart, comparing the length of the bars, to answer these questions.

7. What percentage of housekeeping staff preferred hot drinks? __________

8. What was the most popular drink amongst housekeeping staff? __________

9. What was the least popular drink amongst housekeeping staff? __________

10. What was the least popular drink overall? __________

11. Was it easier to read the length of the bar charts or the height? Give reasons for your answer. __________

____

____

8. Extract information from pictograms 1

Compare information in pictograms.

Numerical information in pictograms is shown using pictures or icons. The icons can represent more than one – this information is given in the key. Each icon always represents the same number. Some pictograms use just one icon, as in this example.

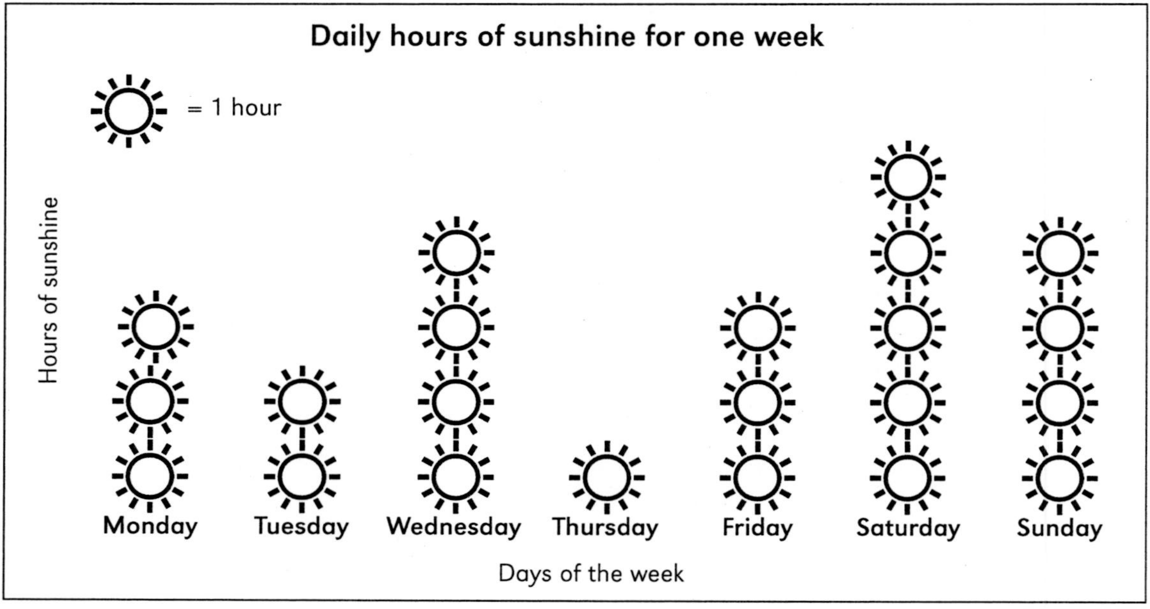

Some pictograms use more than one icon, as in this example:

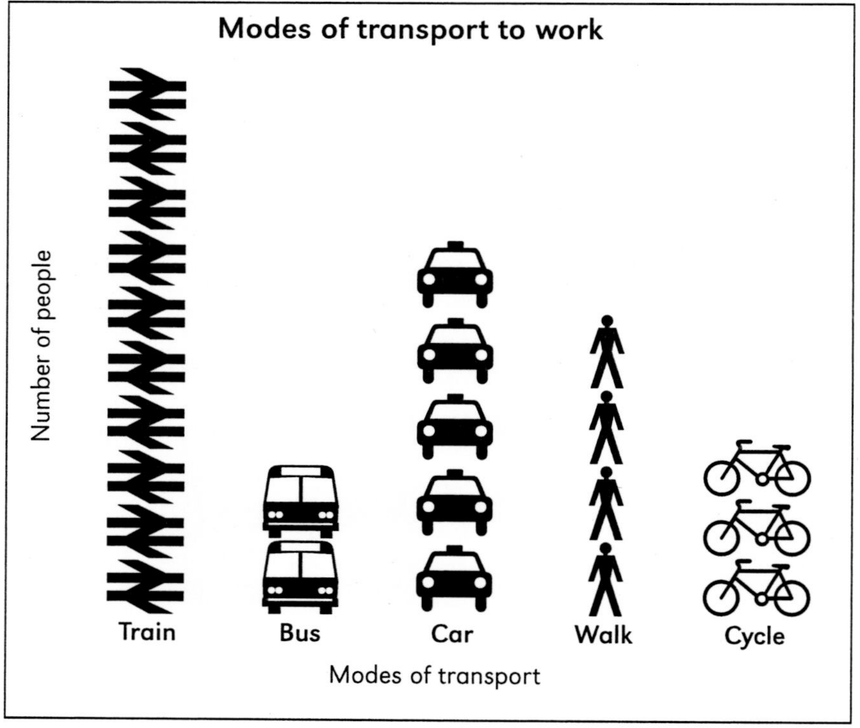

9. Extract information from pictograms 2

skillbuild

Compare information in pictograms.

Use the information in the first pictogram on Worksheet 8 to answer these questions.

1. How many hours of sunshine were there on Monday? ____________
2. How many hours of sunshine were there on Wednesday? ____________
3. Which day had the least hours of sunshine? ____________
4. Which day had the most hours of sunshine? ____________
5. How many hours of sunshine were there over the weekend? ____________

Use the information in the second pictogram to answer these questions.

6. How many people walk to work? ____________
7. How many people cycle to work? ____________
8. How many people drive to work? ____________
9. Which is the most popular method of transport to work? ____________
10. Which is the least popular method of transport to work? ____________

10. Extract information from tables 1

Extract data from tables.

Tables are made up of *rows* and *columns*. Rows go across, whilst columns go down. This table shows the temperature taken on different days in several cities in the UK.

Temperature °C					
City	Mon.	Tues.	Wed.	Thurs.	Fri.
London	19	20	18	22	25
Cardiff	18	16	17	19	19
Glasgow	15	18	19	18	17
Leeds	17	19	20	21	22
Manchester	16	17	17	20	23

Use the information in the table to answer these questions.

1. Which city had the highest temperature on Monday?
2. Which city had the lowest temperature on Thursday?
3. Which city had a temperature of 16°C on Tuesday?
4. How many degrees cooler was it in Glasgow than in London on Friday?
5. How many degrees hotter was it in Cardiff than Manchester on Monday?
6. Which cities were the same temperature on Wednesday?
7. Which was the coldest day overall?
8. Which was the hottest day overall?
9. Which city recorded the highest temperature?
10. Which city recorded the lowest temperature?

11. Extract information from tables 2

Extract data from tables.

This table shows the cost of a 7-day, a 14-day and a 21-day self-catering apartment holiday in four resorts. Use the information in the table to answer the questions.

Resort	7 days	14 days	21 days
Magaluf	£179	£279	£325
Santa Ponca	£365	£445	£499
Cala Mayor	£265	£325	£395
Palma Nova	£228	£299	£349

Prices are per person in a one-bedroom apartment. Flights included.

1. How much does a 14-day holiday in Magaluf cost?
2. How much does a 21-day holiday in Cala Mayor cost
3. How much does a 7-day holiday in Palma Nova cost?
4. Which resort will cost £365 for a 7-day holiday?
5. Which resort will cost £299 for a 14-day holiday?
6. What is the difference in price between a 14-day holiday in Palma Nova and a 14-day holiday in Santa Ponca?
7. What is the difference in price between a 7-day holiday in Cala Mayor and a 7-day holiday in Magaluf?
8. Which two holidays will cost exactly the same amount of money?
9. Which resort is the cheapest overall?
10. Which resort is the most expensive overall?
11. Are flights included in these prices?
12. Are the prices per apartment or per person?

12. Tally charts 1

Count numerical information using a tally.

A *tally chart* is a simple way of collecting data. A tally is a record or count of a number of items. You record the marks with a downward stroke, like this:

| = 1 || = 2 ||| = 3 |||| = 4   ~~||||~~ = 5

When you have written four tallies, the fifth is written as a stroke through the other four. This is sometimes called a *five bar gate*.

This tally chart shows the responses collected in a survey which asked workers about their smoking habits. Use the information in the chart to answer the questions.

Category	Tally
People who smoke	~~||||~~ |
People who do not smoke	~~||||~~ ~~||||~~ ~~||||~~ ~~||||~~ ~~||||~~ ||

1. How many people smoke? [ ]

2. How many people do not smoke? [ ]

3. How many respondents were there altogether? [ ]

4. How many five bar gates were marked? [ ]

13. Tally charts 2

Record numerical information using a tally. Carry out a survey.

When you collect data using a tally chart you need to be clear about the categories you are going to count before you start. For example, if you were asked to conduct a five-minute traffic survey you could categorise the data in several ways:

You could simply count each car with one tally mark:

Number of cars 𝍸 𝍸 𝍸 𝍸 ||

You could count each type of transport by making tally marks in a chart like this one:

Cars	Motobikes	Vans	Lorries	Coaches/buses
𝍸 |	||	|||	𝍸	|

You could count each type of car and mark it by colour:

Blue	Silver	Gold	Green	Red	White	Black	Other
𝍸 𝍸	𝍸 ||	||	||||	𝍸 |	|||	𝍸	|

You are going to make an observation of other members of your class or group and record the information in a tally chart. You need to define the categories of information you are going to record before you start. These could include:

- **hair colour**
- **eye colour**
- **height**
- **gender.**

14. Understanding pie charts 1

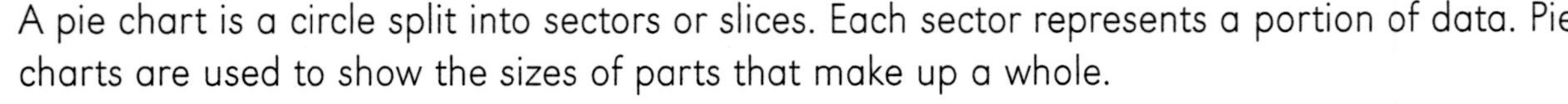

A pie chart is a circle split into sectors or slices. Each sector represents a portion of data. Pie charts are used to show the sizes of parts that make up a whole.

This pie chart shows the results of a survey into the smoking habits of 20 employees in a shop. You can see that most of the employees (75%) are non-smokers. 25% of the employees are smokers.

Employees that smoke

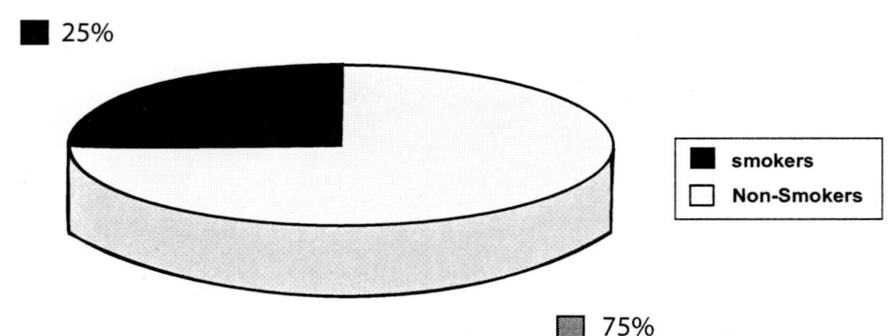

1. How many employees smoke? __________

2. What fraction of employees are non-smokers? __________

3. How many employees are non-smokers? __________

4. What fraction of employees are smokers? __________

15. Understanding pie charts 2

Understand simple pie charts

Pie charts are often used to compare similar sets of data, as the information is often easy to understand in this format.

These pie charts show the modes of transport to work for the 50 employees of a shop.

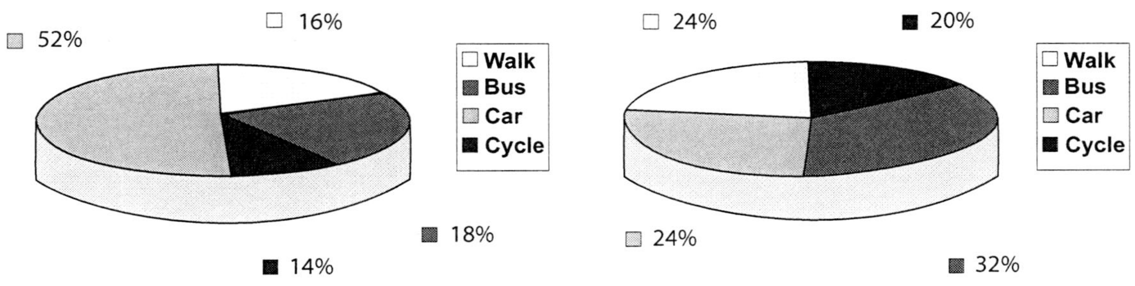

Say whether these statements are true or false.

1. In 2006 14% of employees walked to work.
2. In 2006 more people drove to work than all other forms of transport put together.
3. The mode of transport with the greatest change between 2006 and 2008 is the car.
4. In 2008 the percentage of employees that took a bus and cycled to work was identical.
5. The number of employees who cycled to work increased over two years.
6. In 2008 12 employees drive to work.

16. Hotel – out and about

Follow directions on a map.

There are several tourist attractions near the Old Hall Hotel. Use the map to answer the questions on a separate piece of paper.

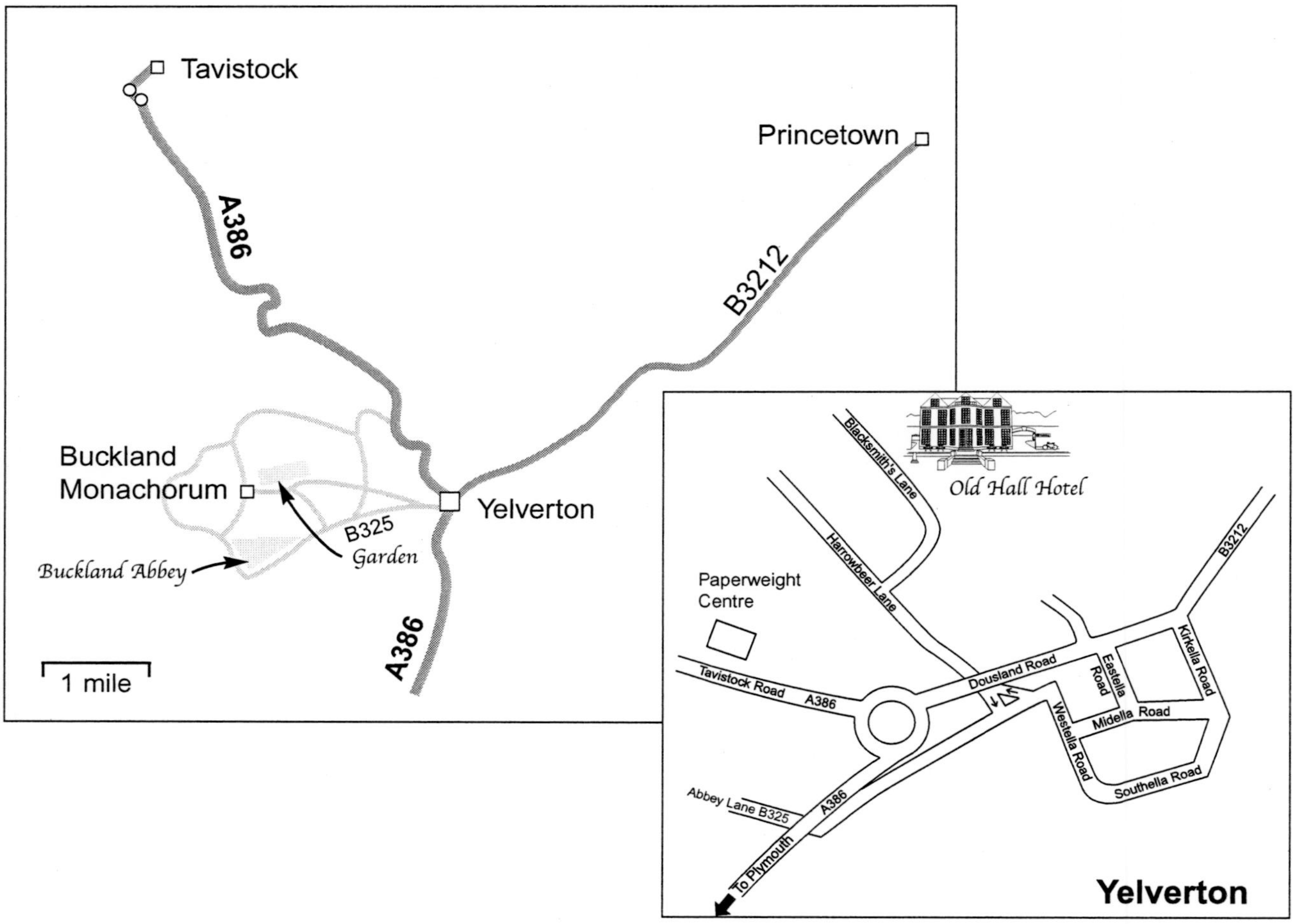

Tavistock
Princetown
A386
B3212
Buckland Monachorum
Yelverton
B325
Garden
Buckland Abbey
A386
1 mile

Old Hall Hotel
Blacksmith's Lane
Harrowbeer Lane
Paperweight Centre
B3212
Tavistock Road A386
Dousland Road
Eastella Road
Kirkella Road
Westella Road
Midella Road
Southella Road
Abbey Lane B325
A386
To Plymouth
Yelverton

1. Describe how to get from the hotel to the Paperweight Centre.
2. Describe how to get from the hotel to Buckland Abbey.
3. What attraction is in the centre of Buckland Monachorum village?
4. Describe how to get from Buckland Abbey to Princetown.
5. What is the road that links Yelverton and Tavistock?
6. Use the scale to work out the distance between Yelverton and Tavistock.

17. Hotel – spa days 1

Extract data from a table. Create a bar chart.

The Old Hall Hotel Leisure Club runs spa days for guests. There are a variety of things to do. Read the information about each activity and carry out the task.

Spa Bath

The Spa Bath is the ideal place to relax after a hard day at work or play! The temperature is kept between 30°C and 40°C. An attendant takes the temperature at 12 noon every day. These are the temperatures for the Spa Bath last week:

Day	Sun.	Mon.	Tues.	Wed.	Thurs.	Fri.	Sat.
Temp°C	31	32	34	38	37	35	36

Present this data as a bar chart.

18. Hotel – spa days 2

Extract data from a timetable. Create a bar chart.

Sauna

Guests can use the sauna throughout the day at the weekends but only during certain hours during the week. Use the information in this table to answer the questions.

The Old Hall Hotel sauna opening times		
	Open	**Closed**
Monday	18.00	21.00
Tuesday	18.00	21.00
Wednesday	16.00	22.00
Thursday	18.00	22.00
Friday	16.00	22.00
Saturday	10.00	23.00
Sunday	10.00	22.00

1. At what time does the sauna open on Mondays? ________________

2. How many hours is the sauna open on Tuesdays? ________________

3. On which weekday is the sauna open for the longest time? ________________

4. For how many hours is the sauna open over the weekend? ________________

Draw a bar chart to show how long the sauna is open on each day.

19. Hotel – spa days 3

Extract data from a list. Create a pictogram.

Yoga

The most popular class on a spa day is the 'Yoga to Mozart' class. These are the numbers who attended this class last week:

Monday	15
Tuesday	20
Wednesday	15
Thursday	10
Friday	15
Saturday	25
Sunday	30

Create a suitable symbol to represent five people and present this data as a pictogram.

20. Hotel – leisure club visitors 1

Extract data from tables.

Leisure club staff keep a daily record of the number of visitors. This table shows the attendance figures at the leisure club for the weeks ending 20th and 27th August 2006. Use the information in the table to answer the questions.

Table 1 – Data for week ending 20 August 2006

Day of the week	Number of visitors
Sunday	115
Monday	121
Tuesday	133
Wednesday	126
Thursday	112
Friday	118
Saturday	200

1. How many people visited the leisure club on Saturday? ______________________
2. How many more people went on Wednesday than on Monday? ______________________
3. How many people visited the leisure club over the weekend? ______________________

This table shows the attendance figures at the leisure club for the weeks ending 20th and 27th August 2006. Use the data to work out the difference in visitor numbers over the two weeks. One has been done for you.

Table 2
Data for last two weeks of August 2006

Day	Week 1 visitors	Week 2 visitors	Difference
Sunday	115	110	–5
Monday	121	119	
Tuesday	133	123	
Wednesday	126	165	
Thursday	112	110	
Friday	118	134	
Saturday	200	115	

21. Hotel – leisure club visitors 2

skillbuild

Extract data from tables. Create a bar chart.

Use the information in Table 2 on Worksheet 20 to answer these questions.

1. Which day had the biggest increase in attendance? ____________________

2. Which day had the biggest decrease in attendance? ____________________

Use the information in Table 2 to draw a bar chart in the space below. Write two sentences to describe the data you present in the bar chart.

22. Hotel – circuit training

Organise written information in tables, pictograms and bar charts.

The leisure centre offers circuit training programmes for guests. This is what one of the fitness instructors told a guest.

"You are in good shape! We can start off with a five-minute stretch as a warm-up followed by ten minutes jogging on the treadmill. You then need to work your way around the circuit doing two minutes on the lateral pull down, three minutes on the bicep curl, four minutes on the abductor, five minutes with the hand weights, ten minutes on the cycle, ten minutes on the rowing machine, and then we'll finish with a five-minute walk on the treadmill and five minutes of stretches. I'll take you through all this on your first session."

This information would be easier to understand in a table. Transfer the information from the paragraph into the table. The first exercise has been completed for you.

Circuit training programme		
	Exercise	**Time**
1	Stretching	5 min
2		
3		
4		
5		
6		
7		
8		
9		
10		
Total exercise time		

Once you have completed the table, use separate pieces of paper to present the data firstly as a pictogram and then as a bar chart.

When you have completed both types of graph, say which method you think is better for presenting this information: a table, a bar chart or a pictogram. Give reasons for your answer.

23. Hotel – website hits

Extract data from a pictogram. Present data in a table and a bar chart.

The Old Hall Hotel has a website. This pictogram shows the number of hits each day last week. A hit is when someone visits the website. The computer represents 50 hits.

Transfer the information in the pictogram to the table and answer the questions.

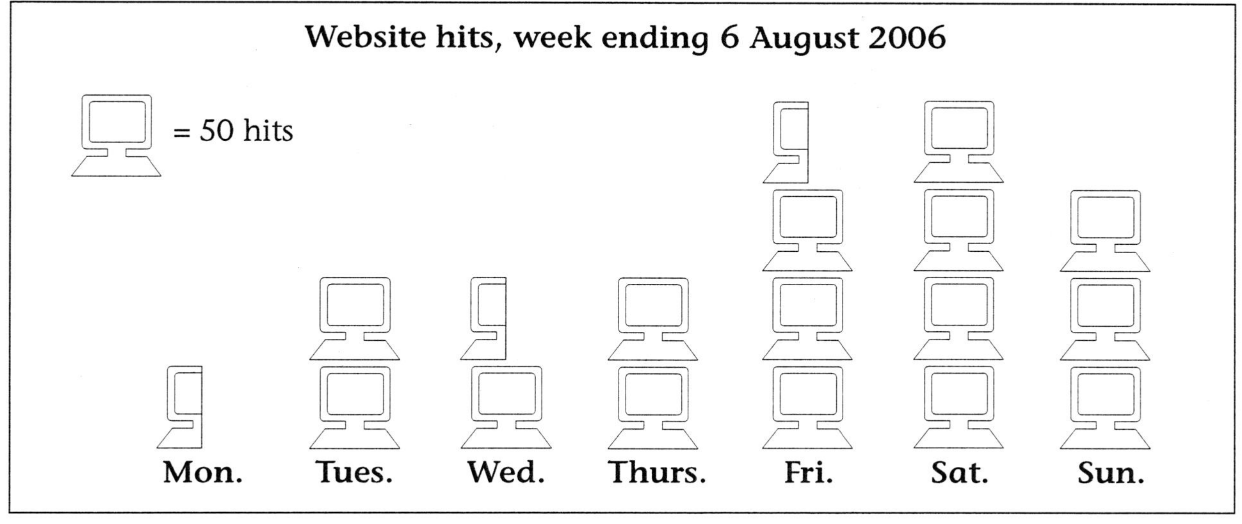

Day	Hits
Monday	
Tuesday	
Wednesday	
Thursday	
Friday	
Saturday	
Sunday	

1. On which day did the least number of people visit the website? ____________________
2. On which day did the most number of people visit the website? ____________________
3. On which two days did the same number of people visit the website? ________________
4. How many more people visited the website on Sunday than on Monday? ____________
5. What was the total number of hits that week? __________________________________

Now present the data in the table as a bar chart.

24. Hotel – late for work!

Extract data from a timetable.

Dev's shift at the Old Hall Hotel begins at 09.00. He gets to work by bus each day. He catches the bus at Bretonside bus station. The hotel is a five-minute walk from the bus stop in Yelverton.

Use the bus timetable to answer the questions.

Monday–Friday	**a.m.**	**a.m.**	**a.m.**	**a.m.**
Bretonside bus station	07.25	07.45	08.00	08.45
Mutley Plain	07.29	07.49	08.04	08.54
Crownhill	07.39	07.59	08.14	09.04
Roborough	07.51	08.11	08.26	09.16
Yelverton	08.01	08.21	08.36	09.26

1. How long is the bus journey from the station to Yelverton?
2. Which bus do you think Dev should catch?
3. Dev lives a five-minute walk from the bus station. What time should he leave home to catch that bus?
4. If Dev missed that bus would he get to work in time if he caught the next one?
5. How long is Dev's total journey time to work each day?
6. Dev works five days a week. How long does he spend travelling to and from work each week?

25. Hotel – birthday lists

Extract data from a list. Use a tally chart. Create a bar chart. Write dates.

The management of the Old Hall Hotel prides itself on its relationship with the staff. Each member of staff receives a birthday card and a small gift from the management on their birthday. This is a list of the birthdays of staff who work in the kitchen.

Staff member	Birthday	Age next birthday
Alex	25th August	54
Val	8th February	32
Dolly	15th September	26
Irene	22nd March	42
Jean-Claude	12th January	53
Jane	3rd August	21
Kevin	28th February	38
Maureen	18th December	24
Liam	14th April	22
John	31st March	19

Re-write the list in date order. The first one has been done for you.

Staff member	Birthday	Age next birthday
Jean-Claude	12th January	53

Sort out the people into groups according to their age. Complete this tally chart and then present the data as a bar chart on a separate piece of paper.

Age	16–19	20–24	25–29	30–34	35–39	40–44	45–50	50+
Tally								

26. Hotel – wedding menus

Extract information from menus. Carry out a survey.

This is a selection of the Old Hall Hotel's buffet menus. Calculate the cost of each of the buffets for 10, 20, 25 and 50 people. Put your answers in the table.

Menu 1 – £7.50 per head
Canapês
Platter of cold meats
Selection of salads
Freshly baked mini-baguettes
Choice of individual desserts

Menu 2 – £8.50 per head
Platter of cold meats
Homemade quiche
Selection of salads
Freshly baked mini-baguettes
Choice of individual desserts

Menu 3 – £9.50 per head
Canapês
Platter of Coronation Chicken
Rice and mango garnish
Selection of salads
Freshly baked mini-baguettes
Choice of individual desserts

Menu 4 – £10.50 per head
Canapês
Platter of cold continental meats
Dressed poached salmon
Selection of salads
Freshly baked mini-baguettes
Choice of individual desserts

Number in party	Menu 1	Menu 2	Menu 3	Menu 4
10	£75.00	£85.00	£95.00	£105.00
20				
25				
50				

Carry out a survey among 20 people to ask them which menu they would prefer. Record your data using a tally chart and present your findings using an appropriate method.

27. Hotel – drink survey

Extract data from a tally chart. Present data in bar charts, pictograms and tables.

Bar staff at the Old Hall Hotel carried out a survey last week. They kept a tally of the drinks sold on each night of the week. Look at the selection of results and carry out the following tasks.

1. **Present the information about bitter in a bar chart.**
2. **Present the information about lager as a pictogram.**
3. **Present the information about white wine in a table.**
4. **Present the information about red wine in either a bar chart, pictogram or table.**

	Bitter	Lager	White wine	Red wine
Monday	卌 卌 |	卌 卌 ||||	卌 卌 卌 |	卌
Tuesday	卌 卌 ||	卌 卌 |	卌 卌 卌 ||||	卌 卌 |||
Wednesday	卌 卌	卌 卌 ||||	卌	卌 卌 |
Thursday	卌 ||	卌 |||	卌 |||	卌 ||||
Friday	卌 卌 卌 卌 卌 ||	卌 卌 卌 卌 卌 卌 ||||	卌 卌 卌 |	卌 卌 卌 卌 ||||
Saturday	卌 卌 卌	卌 卌 卌 ||||	卌 卌 卌 卌 |	卌 卌 卌 卌 卌 |
Sunday	卌 卌 |	卌 卌 ||	卌 卌 ||||	卌 卌 ||

Write a few sentences comparing the information you have presented.

28. Supermarket – free bus

Use a scale to calculate distances. Get information from a map.

Blackwell's provides a free bus from several pick-up points around the local area. This map shows the villages where the bus stops. Use the key to answer the questions on a separate piece of paper.

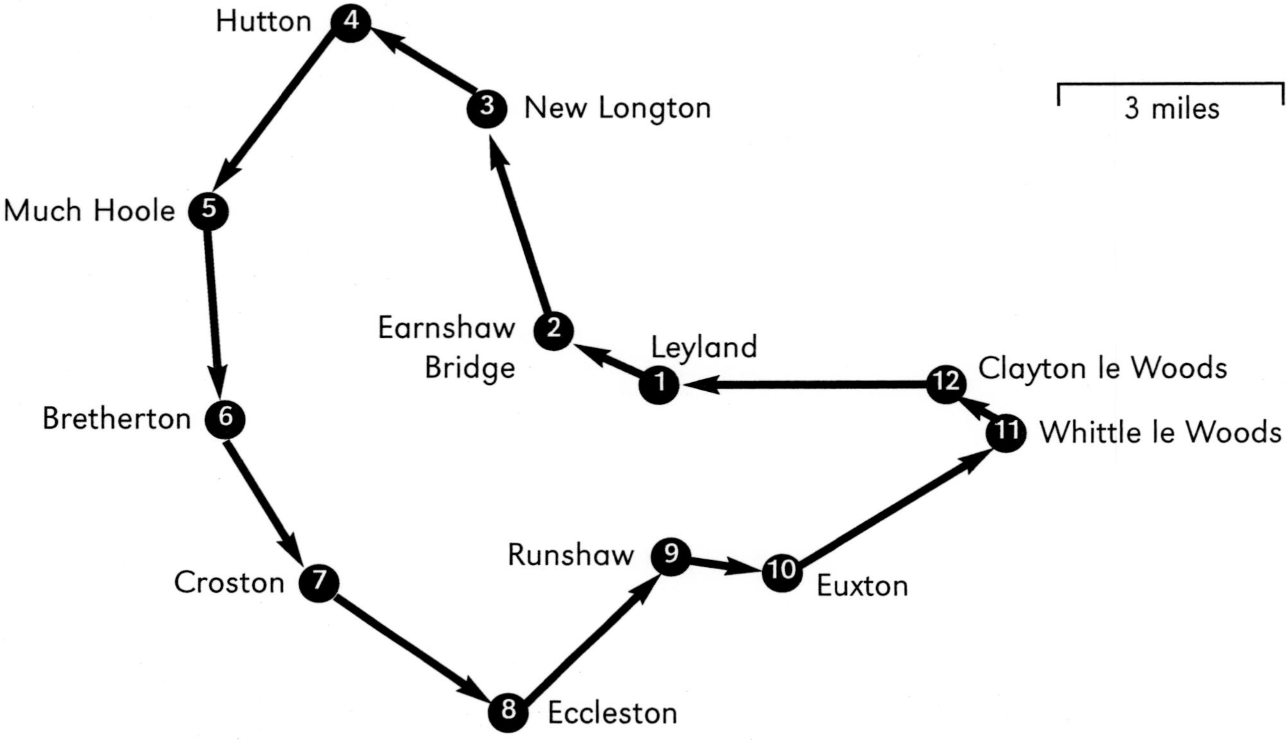

1. How many miles will the bus travel between Earnshaw Bridge and Hutton?
2. How many miles will the bus travel between Much Hoole and Runshaw Moor?
3. At which village does the bus stop first?
4. Which is the last village the bus stops at before getting to Blackwell's?
5. How many villages does the bus stop at?
6. How many miles will the bus travel between Croston and Euxton?
7. How many miles would a direct journey from Croston to Leyland be?
8. How many miles will the bus journey from Croston to Leyland be?
9. What is the total mileage of the round trip?

29. Supermarket – fridge temperatures

Extract information from tables. Create a bar chart.

The fridges in Blackwell's are monitored carefully. These charts show the temperature of each fridge unit over the period of a week. These charts show the temperatures for the milk and cold meat refrigerators last week. Present the data in the charts as a bar chart.

Milk refrigerator

Day	**Sunday**	**Monday**	**Tuesday**	**Wednesday**	**Thursday**	**Friday**	**Saturday**
Temp °C	6	5	4	4	3	4	5

Cold meat refrigerator

Day	**Sunday**	**Monday**	**Tuesday**	**Wednesday**	**Thursday**	**Friday**	**Saturday**
Temp °C	3	3	3	2	2	4	3

Write three statements comparing your bar charts.

1. ______________________________

____

2. ______________________________

____

3. ______________________________

____

30. Supermarket – shopping on the Net 1

Extract information from tables. Create a pictogram.

Blackwell's customers can order their groceries on the Internet. This table shows the number of orders made using Blackwell's website last week.

Day	Sunday	Monday	Tuesday	Wednesday	Thursday	Friday	Saturday
Hits	41	78	61	24	99	78	81

Round each number up or down to the nearest 10.

Day	Sunday	Monday	Tuesday	Wednesday	Thursday	Friday	Saturday
Hits							

Use these numbers and create a pictogram to show off the data. Use a symbol, such as this can [can symbol] to represent either 10 or 20 orders – whichever is most appropriate.

31. Supermarket – shopping on the Net 2

Extract information from a pictogram.

This pictogram shows the number of hits each day last week that did not result in an order. Each whole computer represents 20 hits.

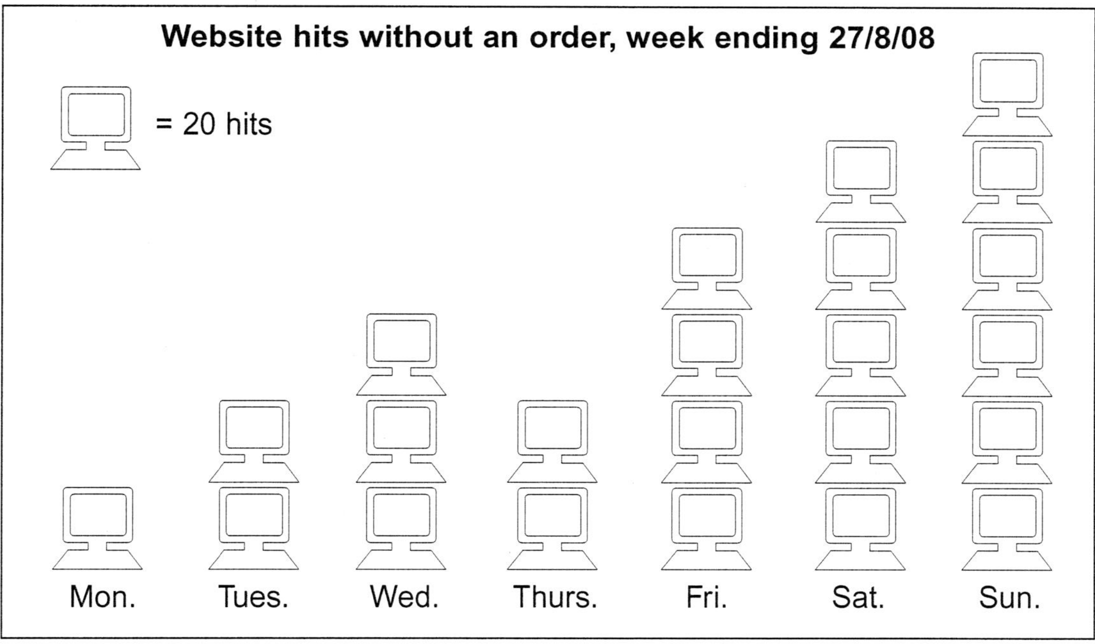

Transfer the information in the pictogram to this table. What information can you work out from the data?

Day	Hits
Monday	
Tuesday	
Wednesday	
Thursday	
Friday	
Saturday	
Sunday	

32. Supermarket – the busiest checkout 1

Extract data from tables. Present data in a table.

The tills at Blackwell's automatically take a record of each transaction. This table shows how many customers used Till 1 for the week ending 23 August 2008. Round the numbers to the nearest 10 then answer the questions.

Table 1

Data for week ending 23 August 2008 Till 1		
Day	**Customers**	**Rounded number**
Monday	218	220
Tuesday	187	
Wednesday	156	
Thursday	219	
Friday	231	
Saturday	228	
Sunday	356	

1. Exactly how many customers used Till 1 on Monday? __________
2. Exactly how many more people used Till 1 on Sunday than on Thursday? __________
3. Use the rounded figures to say how many people used Till 1 over the weekend. __________
4. Use the rounded figures to say how many people used Till 1 over the whole week. __________

This table shows how many customers used Till 2 for the week ending 23 August 2008. Transfer the data for Till 1 and Till 2 to Table 3 on Worksheet 33. Use the data to work out the difference in customer numbers between the tills. One has been done for you.

Table 2

Data for week ending 23 August 2008 Till 2		
Day	**Customers**	**Rounded number**
Monday	198	200
Tuesday	197	
Wednesday	132	
Thursday	234	
Friday	217	
Saturday	292	
Sunday	325	

33. Supermarket – the busiest checkout 2

Extract data from tables. Construct a bar chart.

Table 3

Day	Till 1	Till 2	Difference
Monday	218	198	20
Tuesday			
Wednesday			
Thursday			
Friday			
Saturday			
Sunday			

Use the information in Table 3 to answer these questions.

1. Which day shows the biggest difference between customer numbers? ______________

2. Which day shows the smallest difference between customer numbers? ______________

Use the information in Table 3 to draw a bar chart, then write two sentences to describe the data you present in the bar chart.

1. ____

2. ____

3. ____

34. Supermarket – first aid training

Organise written information in tables and bar charts.

The supermarket trains some of its staff in first aid. This is what the course instructor told a group of trainees.

> "It's 9 a.m. now and we're going to have a cup of coffee first. Can everyone sign the register and be ready to start training at 9.15. The first thing we will do is teach you how to deal with unconsciousness. This will take about 15 minutes. Then we'll go on to spend about 30 minutes on cardiac arrest. Bleeding and wounds will take up the next 30 minutes. We'll have a ten-minute break at 10.30. After the break we'll learn about burns and scalds for about 20 minutes and then we'll spend half an hour learning about electrical injuries.
> We'll learn about dealing with shock at 11.30 – this will take about 20 minutes. Then we'll finish with injuries to bones, muscles and joints. The taught session will end at 12.30. Lunch is from 12.30–1.30. Your multiple choice test will be at 1.45 in the board room."

This information would be easier to understand in a table. Transfer the information from the paragraph into the table. The first task has been completed for you.

First aid training		
	Activity	**Time**
1	Coffee and sign register	9.00 a.m.
2		
3		
4		
5		
6		
7		
8		
9		
10		
11		
Total training time		

Once you have completed the table, use separate pieces of paper to present the data.

When you have completed both types of graph, say which method you think is better for presenting this information: a table or a bar chart. Give reasons for your answer.

35. Supermarket – birthday lists

Extract data from a list. Use a tally chart. Create a bar chart. Read dates.

Blackwell's Supermarket is a family-run firm and the management team sends each member of staff a birthday card and a gift on their birthday. This is a list of the birthdays of staff who work on the deli counter.

Re-write the list in date order and work out the age that the staff member will be next birthday.

Staff member	Birthday	Year of birth	Age next birthday
Bev	1st July	'49	
Ann	26th March	'70	
Jane	11th November	'59	
Fred	2nd March	'63	
John	10th April	'54	
Mary	31st March	'55	
Jenny	15th December	'70	
Ann	1st September	'80	
Penny	15th October	'87	
James	31st January	'52	

	Staff member	Birthday	Age next birthday
1.	James	31st January	
2.			
3.			
4.			
5.			
6.			
7.			
8.			
9.			
10.			

Sort out the people into groups according to their age. Complete this tally chart and then present the data as a bar chart on a separate piece of paper.

Age	16–19	20–24	25–29	30–34	35–39	40–44	45–50	50+
Tally								

36. Supermarket – best buys 1

Extract information from a price list. Create a bar chart.

Blackwell's has a variety of special offers. This week there are special offers on coffee. Use the list of coffee prices to draw a bar chart that compares the prices of the 200 g jars, the prices of the 400 g jars and the prices of the 800 g jars.

Special offer coffee prices

Fine Kenyan Ground Coffee (200 g)	£2.78
Fine Kenyan Ground Coffee (400 g)	£5.48
Fine Kenyan Ground Coffee (800 g)	£10.48
Fine Sumatran Ground Coffee (200 g)	£2.88
Fine Sumatran Ground Coffee (400 g)	£5.68
Fine Sumatran Ground Coffee (800 g)	£10.68
Fine Columbian Ground Coffee (200 g)	£2.92
Fine Columbian Ground Coffee (400 g)	£5.78
Fine Columbian Ground Coffee (800 g)	£10.48

37. Supermarket – best buys 2

Calculate best buys. Create a bar chart.

You can calculate the best buy by working out how much the product costs, like for like. In this case you need to how much each type of coffee costs per 100 g.

1. Fine Kenyan Ground Coffee (200 g) £2.78
   Price per 100 g = £2.79 ÷ 2 = £1.39
2. Fine Kenyan Ground Coffee (400 g) £5.48
   Price per 100 g = £5.48 ÷ 4 = £1.37
3. Fine Kenyan Ground Coffee (800 g) £10.48
   Price per 100 g = £10.48 ÷ 8 = £1.31

So, the cheapest coffee is in the 800 g sized jar.

Use a calculator to work out the cost per 100 g of each of the other types of coffee. Remember to show your working.

1. Fine Sumatran Ground Coffee (200 g)
2. Fine Sumatran Ground Coffee (400 g)
3. Fine Sumatran Ground Coffee (800 g)
4. Fine Columbian Ground Coffee (200 g)
5. Fine Columbian Ground Coffee (400 g)
6. Fine Columbian Ground Coffee (800 g)
7. **Use a separate piece of paper to draw a bar chart to compare the cost per 100 g of each type of coffee.**
8. **Use a separate piece of paper to draw a single bar chart that compares the cost per 100 g of each 200 g sized jar of coffee, each 400 g sized jar of coffee and each 800 g sized jar of coffee.**

38. Supermarket – sandwich survey

Extract data from a tally chart. Present data in bar charts, pictograms and tables.

Café staff at the supermarket carried out a survey last week. They kept a tally of the sandwiches sold on each day of the week. Look at the selection of results and carry out these tasks.

1. **Present the information about tuna and mayonnaise sandwiches in a bar chart.**
2. **Present the information about ham and tomato sandwiches as a pictogram.**
3. **Present the information about egg and cress sandwiches in a table.**
4. **Present the information about cheese and pickle sandwiches in either a bar chart, pictogram or table.**

	Tuna and mayonnaise	Ham and tomato	Egg and cress	Cheese and pickle
Monday	𝍸 𝍸 𝍸 𝍸 𝍸	𝍸 𝍸 𝍸 𝍸 𝍸	𝍸 𝍸 𝍸 𝍷𝍷𝍷𝍷	𝍸 𝍸 𝍸 𝍸 𝍸 𝍸 𝍸 𝍸 𝍸
Tuesday	𝍸 𝍸 𝍸 𝍸 𝍸 𝍸	𝍸 𝍸 𝍸 𝍸 𝍸 𝍸 𝍸	𝍸 𝍸 𝍸 𝍸 𝍸 𝍷𝍷𝍷	𝍸 𝍸 𝍸 𝍸 𝍸 𝍸 𝍸 𝍸 𝍸 𝍸
Wednesday	𝍸 𝍸 𝍸 𝍸 𝍸 𝍸 𝍸 𝍸	𝍸 𝍸 𝍸 𝍸 𝍸 𝍸 𝍸 𝍸 𝍸	𝍸 𝍸 𝍸	𝍸 𝍸 𝍸 𝍸 𝍸 𝍸 𝍸 𝍸 𝍸 𝍸 𝍸
Thursday	𝍸	𝍸 𝍸 𝍸 𝍸 𝍸 𝍸	𝍸 𝍸 𝍸 𝍸 𝍸 𝍷𝍷	𝍸 𝍸 𝍸 𝍸 𝍸 𝍸 𝍸 𝍸 𝍸 𝍸 𝍸 𝍸
Friday	𝍸 𝍸 𝍸 𝍸 𝍸	𝍸 𝍸 𝍸 𝍸 𝍸 𝍸 𝍸	𝍸 𝍸 𝍸 𝍷𝍷𝍷𝍷	𝍸 𝍸 𝍸 𝍸 𝍸 𝍸 𝍸 𝍸 𝍸 𝍸 𝍸
Saturday	𝍸 𝍸 𝍸	𝍸 𝍸 𝍸 𝍸	𝍸 𝍸	𝍸 𝍸 𝍸 𝍸 𝍸
Sunday	𝍸 𝍸	𝍸 𝍸 𝍸	𝍸 𝍸 𝍷𝍷𝍷𝍷	𝍸 𝍸 𝍸 𝍸

Write a few sentences comparing the information you have presented.

39. Supermarket – stock check

Extract data from a tally chart. Present data in bar charts, pictograms and tables.

Orders for the supply of goods are made several times a week at Blackwell's. Staff fill in stock sheets every time they re-fill a shelf so that the right amount of goods can be ordered. This chart shows a stock sheet for the bakery. There are some gaps in the table. Use your maths skills to work out the missing numbers.

Blackwell's replenishment list – Bakery department				
Date	**Item**	**In stock room**	**Number taken**	**Number left**
15.07	White crusty	65		12
	White baps x 6	30	23	
	Brown crusty	55	32	
	Brown baps x 6	35		11
	Baguette	25	8	
	Croissant	40		21
	Scones x 4	25	9	
	Tea cakes x 4	25		13
	Total			

1. Calculate the total number of bakery items taken from the stock room on 15th July.
2. Use a separate piece of paper to draw a bar chart to show the quantities of each of the bakery products taken from the stock room on 15th July.
3. Use a separate piece of paper to draw another bar chart to show the quantity of each of the bakery products left in the stock room when the supermarket closed on 15th July.

40. Factory – deliveries

Use a scale to calculate distances. Get information from a map.

AutoParts delivers goods to its customers. This map shows the route one of the drivers took yesterday. He started his journey at the AutoParts factory. Use the key to answer the questions on a separate piece of paper.

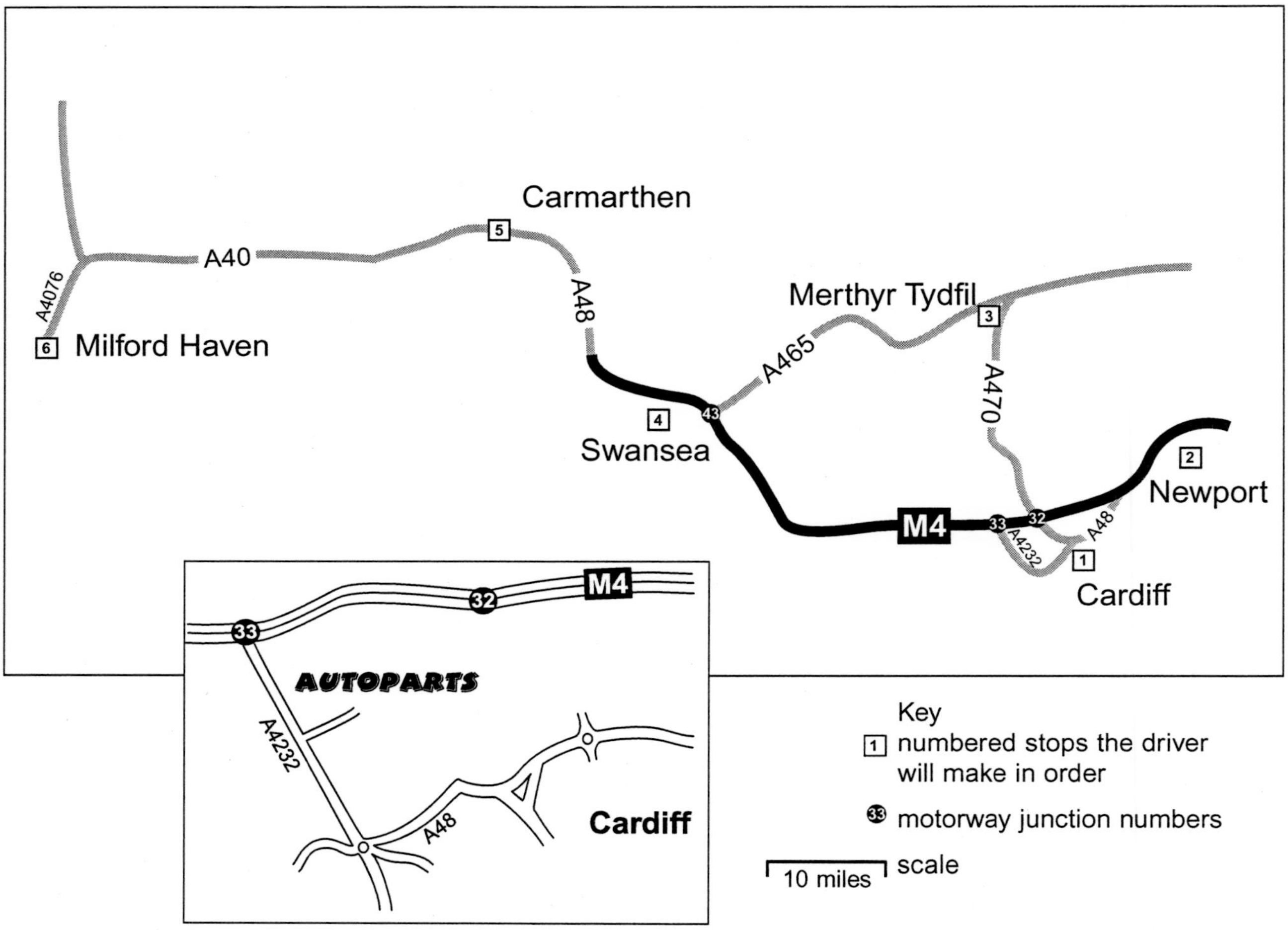

Carmarthen
5
A40
A4076
6 Milford Haven
A48
Merthyr Tydfil
3
A465
A470
43
4
Swansea
M4
33
32
A4232
A48
2
Newport
1
Cardiff

M4
32
33
AUTOPARTS
A4232
A48
Cardiff

Key
1 numbered stops the driver will make in order
33 motorway junction numbers
10 miles scale

1. How many miles will the driver travel between Newport and Merthyr Tydfil?
2. What roads will the driver take between Carmarthen and Milford Haven?
3. At which town will the driver stop first?
4. Which is the last town the driver will stop at before getting back to AutoParts?
5. How many stops will the driver make?
6. How many miles will the driver travel between Merthyr Tydfil and Swansea?
7. How many miles would a direct journey from Swansea to AutoParts be?
8. What is the total mileage of the round trip?

41. Factory – comparing performance

Extract information from a table. Create a bar chart.

AutoParts keeps a record of the value of the goods it sells. This table shows the value of Ford Focus fuel tank sales for 2005 and 2006.

Month	£ 000 in 2005	£ 000 in 2006
January	225	325
February	235	345
March	330	300
April	350	375
May	365	385
June	385	400
July	410	405
August	435	410
September	390	400
October	415	420
November	410	420
December	350	375

Use this data to draw one bar chart which shows both sets of figures.
Hint: You will need to draw two bars for each month. Your chart will look something like this:

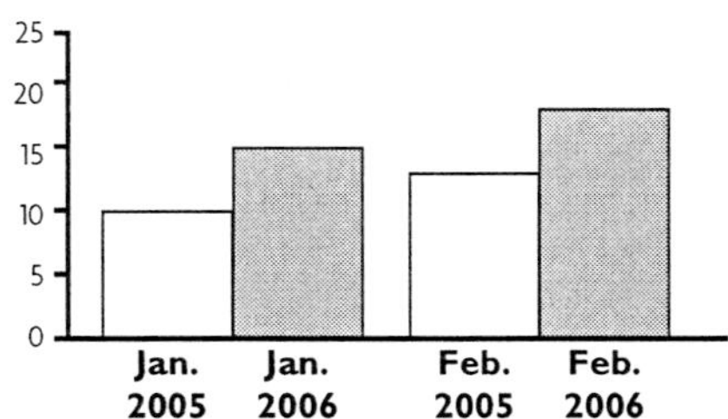

Write two or three sentences summarising the information in the bar chart.

42. Factory – courier service

skillbuild

Count tally marks. Calculate courier charges.

AutoParts sent a large consignment to a customer on Friday. The parcels contained sets of seals for a variety of cars. The packs were roughly the same size but their weights were slightly different. This tally chart shows the number of parcels that were sent. Count up the tally marks and fill in the numbers in the chart. Then answer the questions.

Weight	**40 kg**	**41 kg**	**42 kg**	**43 kg**	**44 kg**	**45 kg**
Tally	IIII	𝍸 IIII	𝍸 𝍸	𝍸 IIII	𝍸 II	III
Number						

1. How many parcels were in the total consignment? ________________

2. How many parcels weighed 43 or more kilos? ________________

3. How many parcels weighed less than 43 kilos? ________________

4. The cost of posting a parcel of this weight is a set cost of £8 per parcel up to 40 kg, plus an extra £1.50 per kilo after that. Work out the cost of posting each of these parcels.

Weight	**40 kg**	**41 kg**	**42 kg**	**43 kg**	**44 kg**	**45 kg**
Cost						

5. Now work out the total cost of sending this consignment. Use a calculator to check your answer.

43. Factory – vending machine

Extract data from a table. Create a pictogram and a bar chart.

There is a vending machine in the reception area at AutoParts. This table shows the number of drinks dispensed from the vending machine last week.

Drink	Tea	Coffee	Chocolate	Soup	Water
Number	96	120	84	48	60

This symbol represents six drinks.

Complete this pictogram to show the number of drinks dispensed last week.

Number of drinks

Tea **Coffee** **Chocolate** **Soup** **Water**

Drinks

Using a separate piece of paper, present the data in the table as a bar chart.

44. Factory – birthday lists

Extract data from a list. Use a tally chart. Create a bar chart. Read dates.

This is a list of the birthdays of some of the staff who work at AutoParts. Re-write the list in chronological order and work out the age the staff member will be next birthday. The first one has been done for you.

Staff member	Birthday	Year of birth	Age next birthday
Pete	3rd May	'67	
Dan	26th March	'70	
Mo	11th November	'59	
Tony	31st March	'55	
Mike	15th December	'70	
Mandy	12th September	'80	
Sue	1st July	'49	
Phil	2nd January	'52	
David	15th March	'75	
Sanjay	2nd April	'82	

	Staff name	Birthday	Age next birthday
1.	Phil	2nd January	
2.			
3.			
4.			
5.			
6.			
7.			
8.			
9.			
10.			

Sort out the people into groups according to their age. Complete this tally chart and then present the data as a bar chart on a separate piece of paper.

Age	16–19	20–24	25–29	30–34	35–39	40–44	45–50	50+
Tally								

45. Factory – fire safety training

Organise written information in tables and bar charts.

Some of the factory staff are being trained in fire safety. This is what the course instructor said at the beginning of the training session:

> "Welcome everyone. It's now 1 p.m. We're going to have a cup of coffee and register first. Can everyone sign the register and be ready to start training at 1.15, please. The total training time is two and a half hours. The first thing we will do is to raise your awareness of fire hazards. That will take about 15 minutes. Then we'll take a ten-minute walk around the production area of the factory and look at good housekeeping. When we get back to the training room we will spend the next 25 minutes discussing fire procedures and raising the alarm. We will then carry out an evacuation procedure. This will take ten minutes.
> After the evacuation I'll show you the different types of fire extinguishers and their uses. This will take about 45 minutes.
> Then we'll have a 15-minute break before we go on to discuss types of fires. This will take about 20 minutes. Then we will go outside for a hands-on session looking at the practical use of fire extinguishers with live fire. The training will end at 4 p.m."

This information would be easier to understand in a table. Transfer the information from the paragraph into the table. The first task has been completed for you.

Fire safety training		
	Activity	**Time**
1	Coffee and sign register	1.00 pm
2		
3		
4		
5		
6		
7		
8		
9		
10		
	Total training time	

Once you have completed the table, use separate pieces of paper to present the data as a bar chart. When you have completed both types of graph, say which method you think is better for presenting this information: a table or a bar chart. Give reasons for your answer.

46. Factory – party buffet

Extract information from pricelists. Count tally marks.

The AutoParts Summer Party is usually held at a local hotel. The menu is based on a selection of buffets. This is the buffet selection for last summer. The hotel receptionist took a tally of the menus chosen. Use the information in the tally chart and the menus to carry out the tasks.

Menu 1 – £7.95 per head
Platter of cold meats
Selection of salads
Freshly baked baguettes
Ice cream
Trifle
Cheese board

Menu 2 – £8.75 per head
Chicken tikka
Rice salad
Naan bread and onion bhajis
Fruit salad
Gateaux
Cheese board
Fresh fruit

Menu 3 – £9.50 per head
Continental meats
Selection of salads
Freshly baked baguettes
Apple pie and ice cream
Gateaux
Cheese board

Menu 4 – £10.50 per head
Crab cakes
Mini tartlets
Homemade quiche
Salad selection
Chicken satay
Bruschetta
Pavlova
Fresh fruit salad and cream
Cheese board

Count up the tallies to find the total number of each menu ordered. Use a calculator to work out the total cost of each of these menus.

	£7.95	£8.75	£9.50	£10.50
Tally	卌 卌 卌 卌 卌 卌 卌 卌 卌 ||||	卌 卌 卌 卌 卌 卌 卌	卌 卌 卌 卌 卌 卌 卌 卌 卌 卌 卌 卌 卌 卌 ||||	卌 卌 卌 卌 卌 卌 卌 卌 卌 卌 卌 卌 |||
Number				
Cost				

47. Factory – new uniforms

Extract data from a table. Count data. Create a bar chart.

AutoParts are ordering new overalls for production staff. Staff have filled in a form to tell the Personnel Department the size of overalls they need. Here is a list of the sizes of production workers on Lines 1–4. Use the information to fill in the uniform requisition form.

Name	**Size**
Dan	L
David	XXL
Gemma	M
Henry	L
Jane	XS
Jez	L
Joe	XL
Mandy	S
Mike	XXL
Mike C	XXXL
Mo	S
Pat	XXL
Pete	L
Tony	XL

Key:
XS = extra small
S = small
M = medium
L = large
XL = extra large
XXL = extra extra large
XXXL = extra extra extra large

Uniform requisition form – Production lines 1–4	
Size	**Quantity**
XS	
S	
M	
L	
XL	
XXL	
XXXL	

Draw a bar chart to show the number of people on Production Lines 1–4 who need these sizes of overalls.

48. Factory – website

Extract information from a bar chart and table. Create a bar chart.

AutoParts has a new website. This bar chart shows the number of visits or hits to the website over the last week. Use the bar chart to answer the questions.

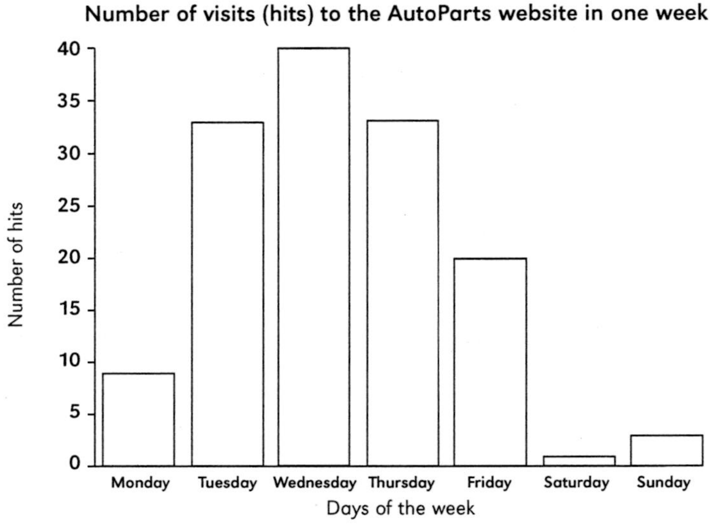

1. On which days did more than 25 people visit the website? ____________
2. To the nearest 10, how many people visited the website on Monday? ____________
3. How many more people visited on Wednesday than on Friday? ____________
4. Which two days had the same number of hits? ____________

The web designer who set up the website has put in a bill for 30 hours' work. This table shows the exact number of hours she spent working on the site. Use the information in the table to carry out the tasks.

Day	Number of hours
Monday	4½
Tuesday	5
Wednesday	3½
Thursday	6
Friday	7
Saturday	5

Draw a bar chart to show how many hours the web designer worked on the site each day.

5. Did she do 30 hours in total?

49. Factory – rates of pay

Count tally marks. Make observations and collect information using a tally. Create a pictogram or a bar chart.

This tally chart shows the number of staff on certain rates of pay at AutoParts. Count up the tally marks and complete the table.

Hourly rate	Tally	Total
£5.55	𝍸 𝍸 𝍸	
£6.15	𝍸 𝍸 𝍸 𝍸 𝍸 III	
£6.25	𝍸 𝍸 𝍸 IIII	
£6.75	𝍸 𝍸	
£7.50	𝍸 𝍸 𝍸 𝍸 𝍸 𝍸 𝍸 𝍸 II	

Use the data to draw a block graph showing the number of AutoParts staff who earn these rates of pay.

You are going to carry out a questionnaire with other members in your class or group and record the results in a tally chart. You need to define the categories of information you are going to record before you start. You need to find out:

- **how far they travel to class**
- **how they get to class.**

Present a summary of your tally chart as either a pictogram or a bar chart.

50. Factory – milometer readings

Extract data from a table. Present data in a bar chart.

At the end of each shift AutoParts delivery drivers complete a mileage log to note their daily mileage. The following mileage logs are for two of the vans. Calculate the total mileage from the tachometer readings. The first one has been done for you.

AUTOPARTS DELIVERY				Van 1 DY03TDR
Date	Driver	TACHOMETER READING		
		Out of yard	Into yard	MILEAGE
7th April	K. Patton	10273	10397	124
8th April		10397	10524	
9th April		10524	10639	
10th April		10639	10727	
11th April		10727	10856	
TOTAL				

AUTOPARTS DELIVERY				Van 2 PT03XCD
Date	Driver	TACHOMETER READING		
		Out of yard	Into yard	MILEAGE
7th April	B. Boskov	9836	9976	
8th April		9976	10125	
9th April		10125	10199	
10th April		10199	10278	
11th April		10278	10387	
TOTAL				

Use a separate piece of paper to draw a single bar chart that will show the daily mileage by both vans. Write two sentences to summarise the data in your bar chart.

51. Factory – parking spaces

Extract data from a pictogram.

AutoParts has a large car park. This pictogram shows how many spaces were used on each day of the week ending 27th August 2006. The car represents 20 car parking spaces. Transfer the information in the pictogram to the table and answer the questions.

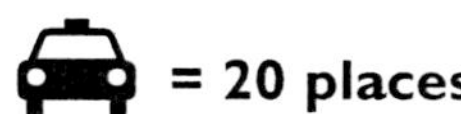

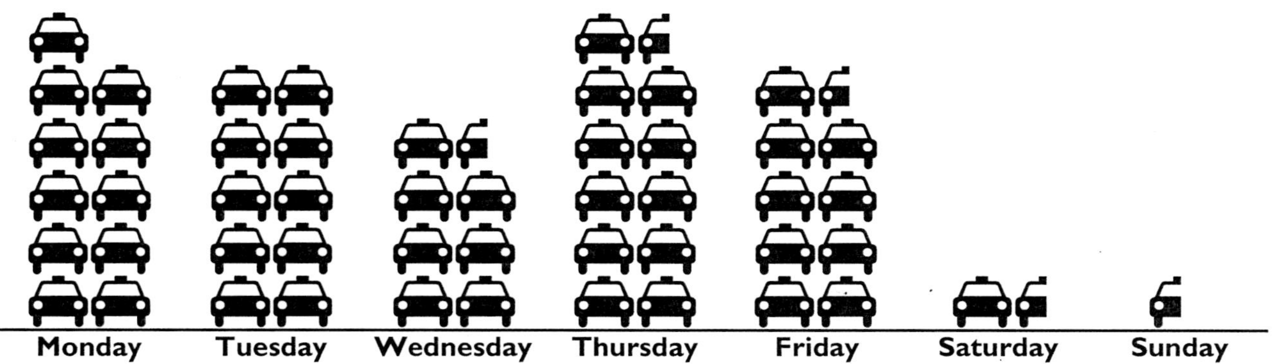

Day	Spaces
Monday	
Tuesday	
Wednesday	
Thursday	
Friday	
Saturday	
Sunday	

1. On which day did the car park have the least empty spaces? ____________

2. On which day did the car park have the most empty spaces? ____________

3. How many more cars used the car park on Tuesday than on Friday? ____________

4. What was the total number of car parking spaces used that week? ____________

1. Presenting data

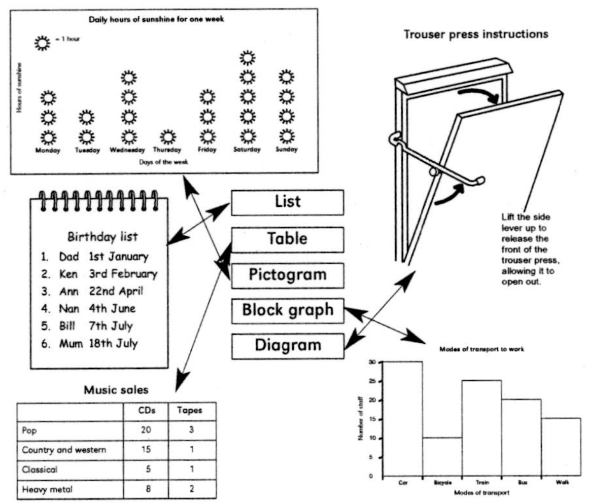

	CDs	Tapes
Pop	20	3
Country and western	15	1
Classical	5	1
Heavy metal	8	2

2. Labelling data 1

1. Music sales
2. Modes of transport to work
3. Daily hours of sunshine for one week
4. Trouser press instructions
5. CDs, tapes, pop, country and western, classical and heavy metal
6. Hours of sunshine and days of the week
7. The number of staff and chosen modes of transport
8. One sun equals one hour of sunshine
9. A key would not be useful on any of the other data in this instance.

3. Labelling data

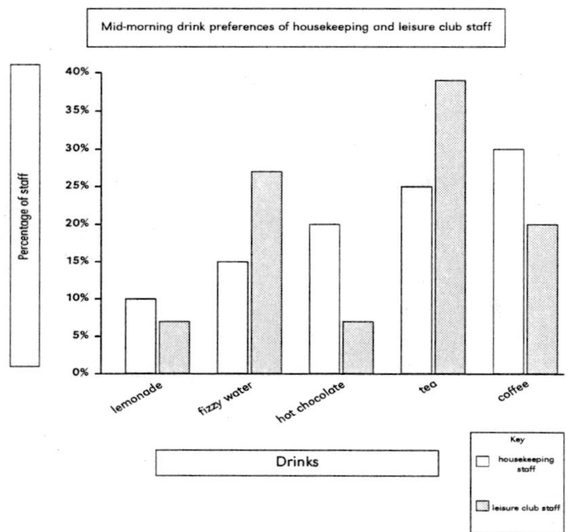

4. Using scale 1

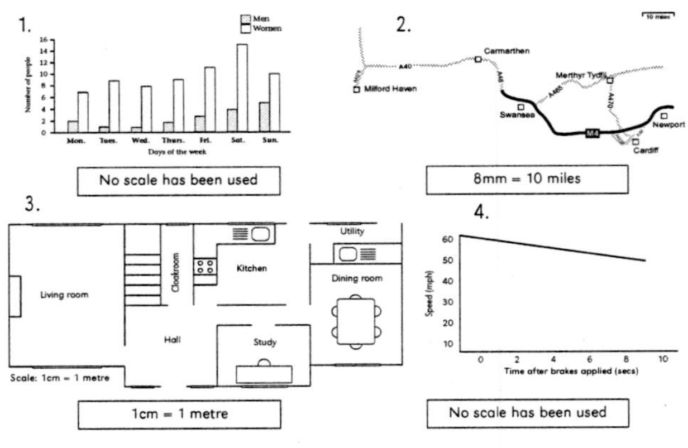

5. Using scale 2

1. 2.5 m
2. 6 m
3. 5 m
4. 6 m
5. 5 m
6. 200 cm
7. 100 cm
8. 150 cm
9. 200 cm
10. 200 cm
11. 22 m

7. Extract information from bar charts 2

1. 39%
2. Approximately 33%
3. tea
4. hot chocolate
5. tea
6. 10%
7. 75%
8. Coffee
9. Lemonade
10. Lemonade

9. Extract information from pictograms 2

1. 3 hours
2. 4 hours
3. Thursday
4. Saturday
5. 9 hours
6. 4
7. 3
8. 5
9. train
10. bus

10. Extract information from tables 1

1. London
2. Glasgow
3. Cardiff
4. 8°C
5. 2°C
6. Cardiff and Manchester
7. Monday
8. Friday
9. London
10. Glasgow

11. Extract information from tables 2

1. £279
2. £395
3. £228
4. Santa Ponca
5. Palma Nova
6. £146
7. £86
8. 14 days in Cala Mayor and 21 days in Magaluf
9. Magaluf
10. Santa Ponca
11. Yes
12. Per person

12. Tally charts 1

1. 6
2. 27
3. 33
4. 6

13. Tally charts 2

You should check your answers with your teacher.

14. Understanding pie charts 1

1. 5 employees smoke.
2. 3/4 of employees are non-smokers.
3. 15 employees are non-smokers.
4. 1/4 of employees are smokers.

15. Understanding pie charts 2

1. False
2. True
3. True
4. False
5. True
6. True

16. Hotel – out and about

1. Turn left as you exit the Old Hall Hotel, go down Blacksmith's Lane and turn left down Harrowbeer Lane. When you reach the junction to Dousland Road, turn right. Take the first right on the roundabout and the Paperweight Centre is in the right.

2. Turn left as you exit the Old Hall Hotel, go down Blacksmith's Lane and turn left down Harrowbeer Lane. When you reach the junction to Dousland Road go straight over then turn right. Follow the road until you get onto the B325, Abbey Lane. Keep following this road and Buckland Abbey is the third exit on the left.

3. There is a garden in the centre of Buckland Monachorum.

4. From Buckland Abbey turn left down the B325 heading towards Yelverton. Once in Yelverton town centre, stay on the same road, you will turn on a 90 degree bend as the road becomes Westalla Road, this will then turn into Southella Road and finally Kirkella Road. When you reach the end of Kirkella Road turn right down the B3212 until you reach Princetown.

5. The road that links Yelverton and Tavistock is the A386.

6. The distance between Yelverton and Tavistock is approximately 7 miles.

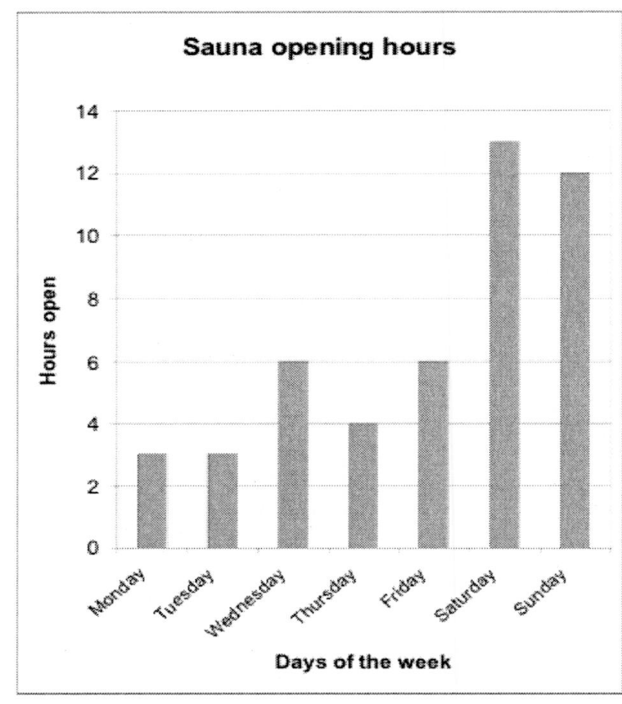

17. Hotel – spa days 1

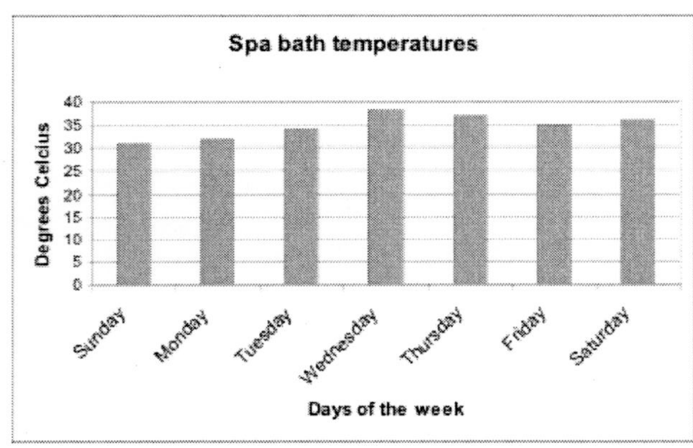

18. Hotel – spa days 2

1. 18.00
2. 3 hours
3. Wednesdays and Fridays.
4. 25 hours

19. Hotel – spa days 3

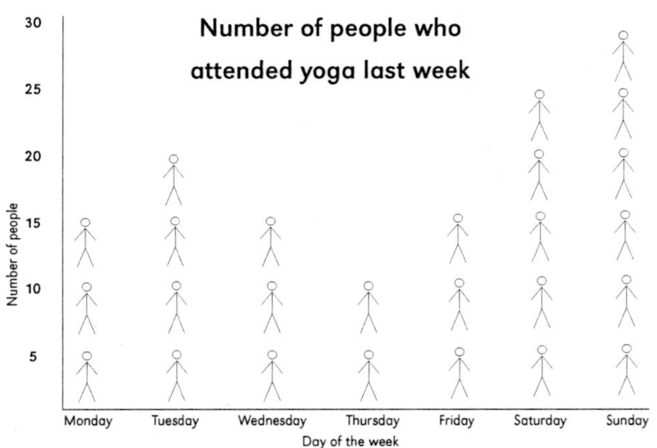

20. Hotel – leisure club visitors 1

1. 200 people
2. 5 people
3. 315 people

Day	Week 1 visitors	Week 2 visitors	Difference
Sunday	115	110	-5
Monday	121	119	-2
Tuesday	133	123	-10
Wednesday	126	165	+39
Thursday	112	110	-2
Friday	118	134	+16
Saturday	200	115	-85

21. Hotel – leisure club visitors 2

1. Wednesday
2. Saturday

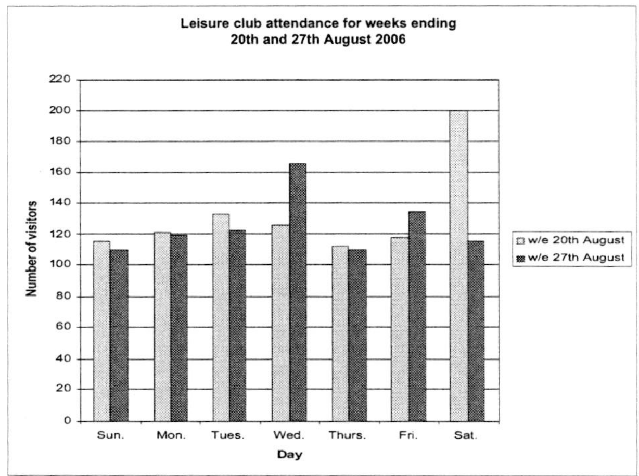

22. Hotel – circuit training

Circuit training programme		
	Exercise	Time
1	Stretching	5 min
2	Jogging on treadmill	10 min
3	Lateral pull down	2 min
4	Bicep curl	3 min
5	Abductor	4 min
6	Hand weights	5 min
7	Cycling	10 min
8	Rowing machine	10 min
9	Treadmill	5 min
10	Stretches	5 min
Total exercise time		59 min

Pictogram of leisure centre circuit training programme

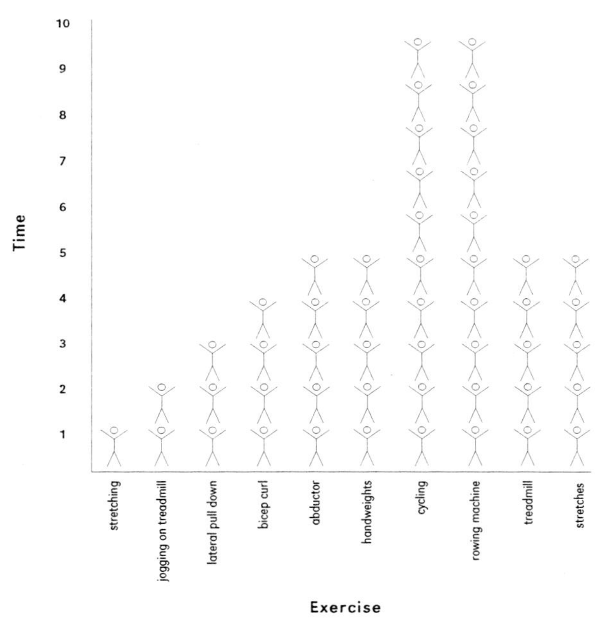

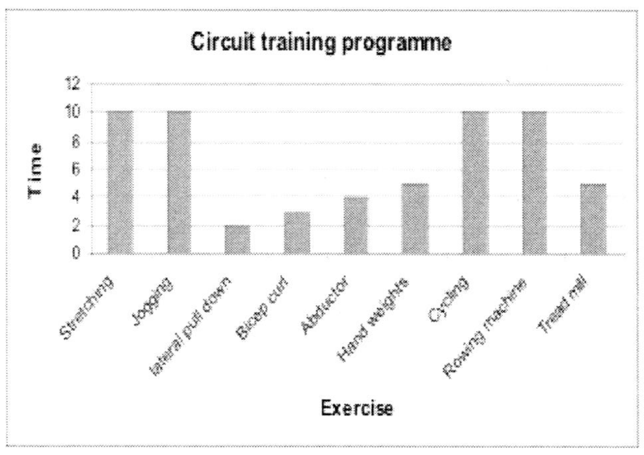

23. Hotel – website hits

Day	Hits
Monday	25
Tuesday	100
Wednesday	75
Thursday	100
Friday	175
Saturday	200
Sunday	150

1. Monday 2. Saturday 3. Tuesday and Thursday
4. 125 people 5. 825 people

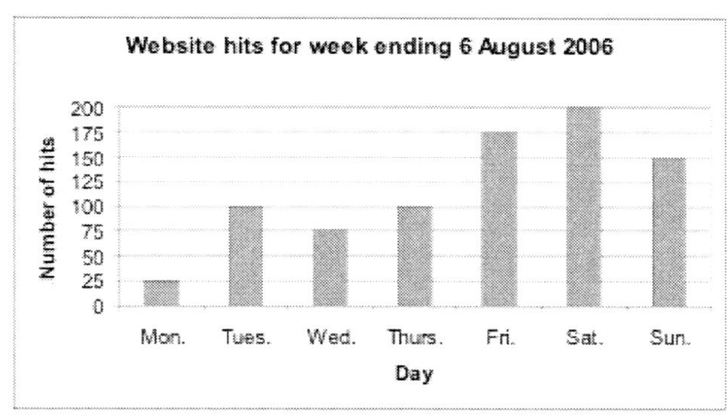

24. Hotel – late for work!

1. 33 minutes
2. Dev should catch the 08.00 bus.
3. 07.55
4. No
5. 46 minutes
6. 7 hours 40 minutes

25. Hotel – birthday lists

Staff member	Birthday	Age next birthday
Jean-Claude	12th January	53
Val	8th February	32
Kevin	28th February	38
Irene	22nd March	42
John	31st March	19
Liam	14th April	22
Jane	3rd August	21
Alex	25th August	54
Dolly	15th September	26
Maureen	18th December	24

Age	16–19	20–24	25–29	30–34	35–39	40–44	45–50	50+
Tally	I	III	I	I	I	I		II

26. Hotel – wedding menus

Number in party	Menu 1	Menu 2	Menu 3	Menu 4
10	£75.00	£85.00	£95.00	£105.00
20	£150.00	£170.00	£190.00	£210.00
25	£187.50	£212.50	£237.50	£262.50
50	£375.00	£425.00	£475.00	£525.00

You should discuss the findings from your survey with your teacher.

27. Hotel – drink survey

1.

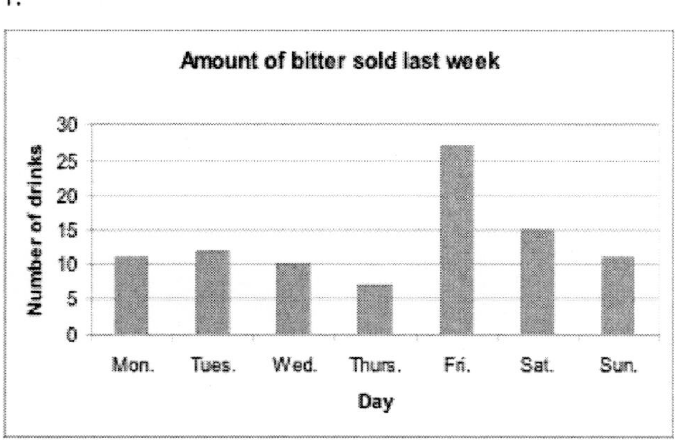

2.

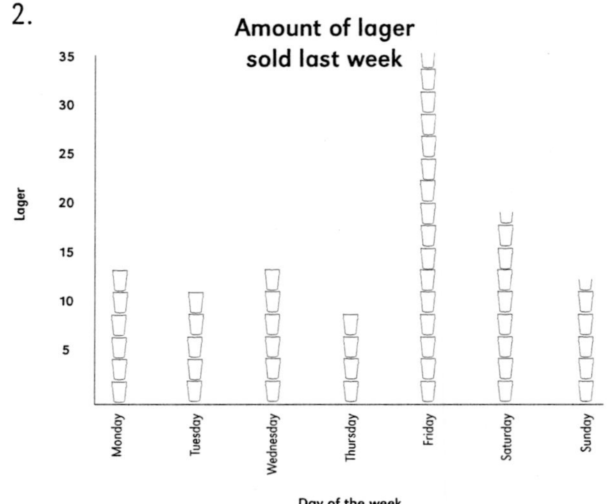

3.

Day of the week	Amount of white wine sold
Monday	16
Tuesday	19
Wednesday	5
Thursday	8
Friday	16
Saturday	21
Sunday	14

4. You should discuss your answer with your teacher.

28. Supermarket – free bus

1. 5 miles
2. 11.5 miles
3. Earnshaw Bridge
4. Clayton le Woods
5. 11
6. 7 miles
7. 5 miles
8. 15 miles
9. 28 miles

29. Supermarket – fridge temperatures

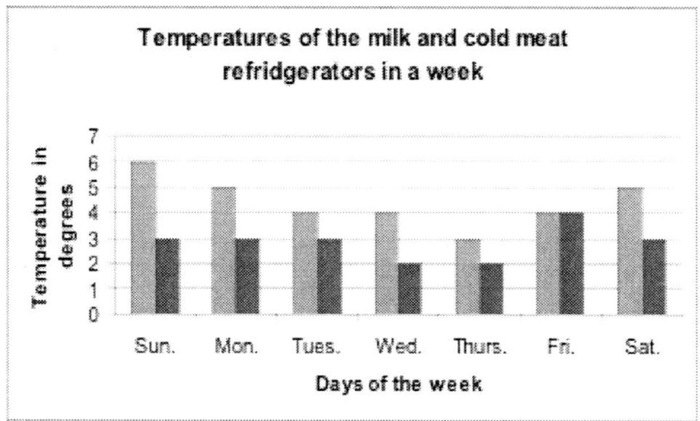

You should discuss your statements with your teacher.

30. Supermarket – shopping on the Net 1

Day	Sunday	Monday	Tuesday	Wednesday	Thursday	Friday	Saturday
Hits	40	80	60	20	100	80	80

Number of orders made using Blackwell's website

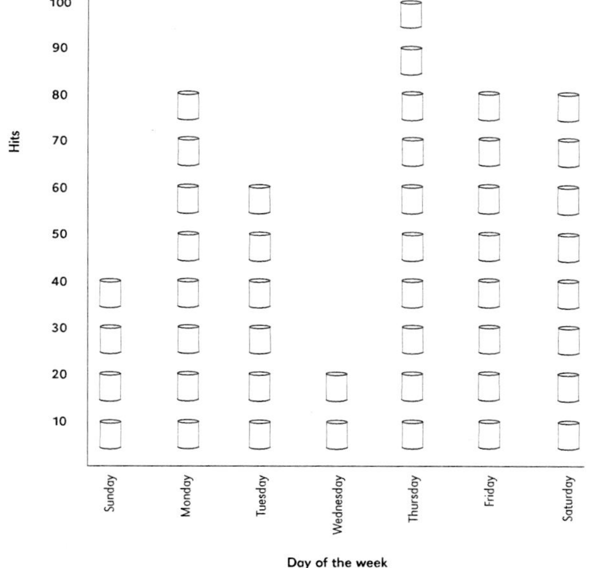

31. Supermarket – shopping on the Net 2

Day	Hits
Monday	20
Tuesday	40
Wednesday	60
Thursday	40
Friday	80
Saturday	100
Sunday	120

It is possible to see from the data that the website had the most hits on the weekend.

32. Supermarket – the busiest checkout 1

Data for week ending 23 August 2008 Till 1		
Day	Customers	Rounded number
Monday	218	220
Tuesday	187	190
Wednesday	156	160
Thursday	219	220
Friday	231	230
Saturday	228	230
Sunday	356	360

1. 218
2. 137 more people
3. 590 people
4. 1610 people

33. Supermarket – the busiest checkout 2

Day	Till 1	Till 2	Difference
Monday	218	198	20
Tuesday	187	197	10
Wednesday	156	132	24
Thursday	219	234	15
Friday	231	217	14
Saturday	228	292	64
Sunday	356	325	31

1. Saturday
2. Tuesday

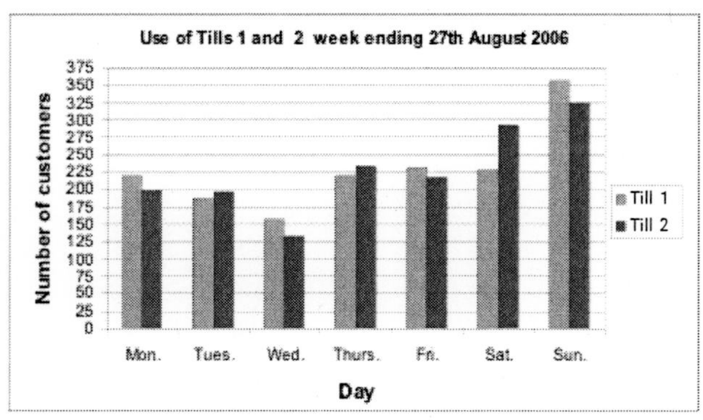

34. Supermarket – first aid training

	First aid training	
	Activity	Time
1	Coffee and sign register	9.00 a.m.
2	Dealing with unconsciousness	9.15 am
3	Cardiac arrest	9.30 am
4	Bleeding and wounds	10.00 am
5	Break	10.30 am
6	Burns and scalds	10.40 am
7	Electrical injuries	11.00 am
8	Dealing with shock	11.30 am
9	Injuries to bones, muscles and joints	11.50 am
10	Lunch	12.30 pm
11	Test	1.45 pm
Total training time		4 hours 45 minutes

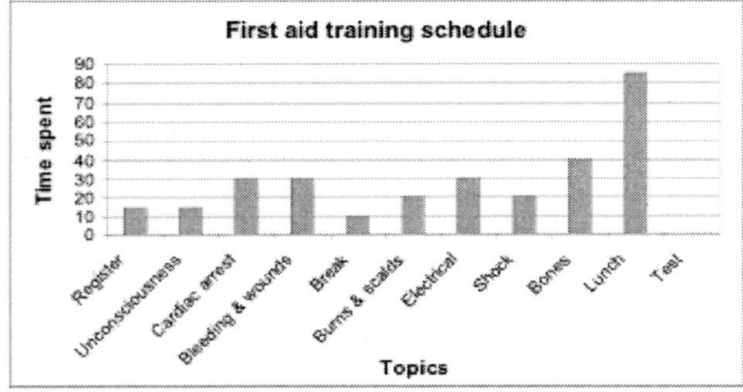

35. Supermarket – birthday lists

You should check your answers to all these questions with your teacher.

36. Supermarket – best buys 1

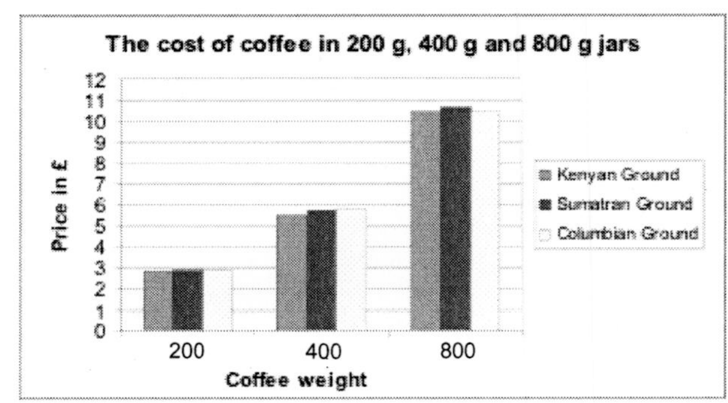

37. Supermarket – best buys 2

1. £2.88 ÷ 2 = £1.44
2. £5.68 ÷ 4 = £1.42
3. £10.68 ÷ 8 = £1.34
4. £2.92 ÷ 2 = £1.46
5. £5.78 ÷ 4 = £1.45
6. £10.48 ÷ 8 = £1.31
7.

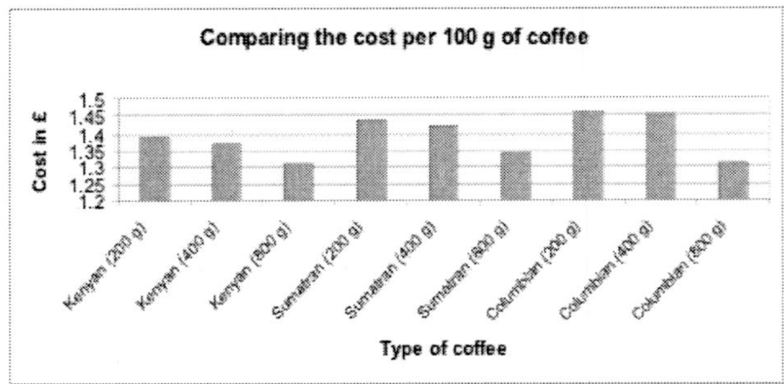

8.

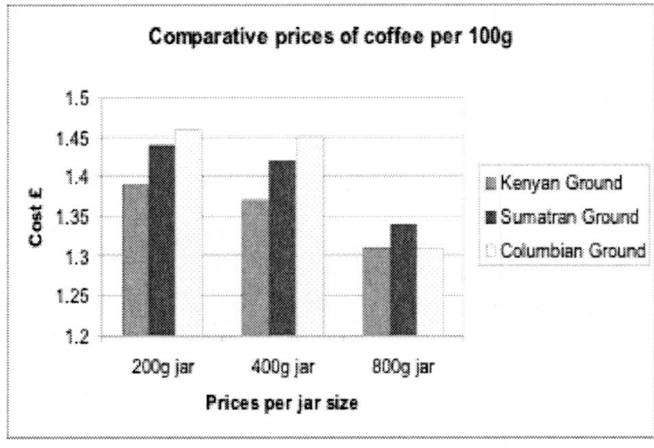

38. Supermarket – sandwich survey

1.

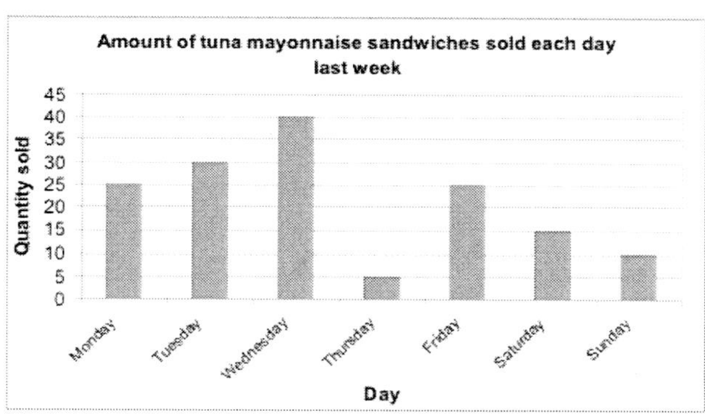

2.

Amount of ham and tomato sandwiches sold each day last week

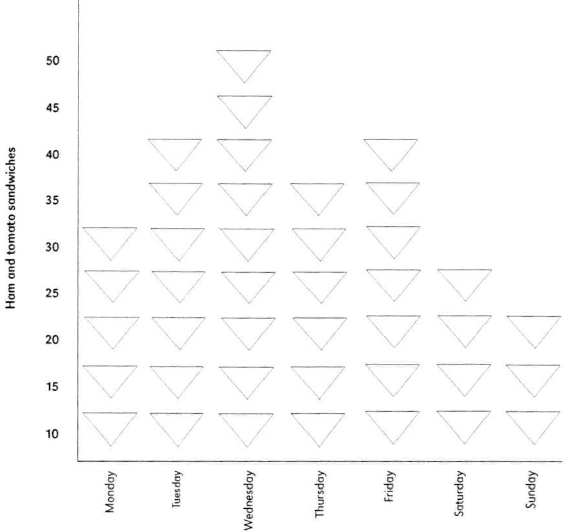

Days of week

3.

Day	Amount of egg and cress sandwiches sold
Monday	19
Tuesday	28
Wednesday	15
Thursday	27
Friday	19
Saturday	10
Sunday	14

4. You should check your answers with your teacher.

39. Supermarket – stock check

Blackwell's replenishment list – Bakery department				
Date	Item	In stock room	Number taken	Number left
15.07	White crusty	65	53	12
	White baps x 6	30	23	7
	Brown crusty	55	32	23
	Brown baps x 6	35	24	11
	Baguette	25	8	17
	Croissant	40	19	21
	Scones x 4	25	9	16
	Tea cakes x 4	25	12	13
	Total	300	180	120

2.

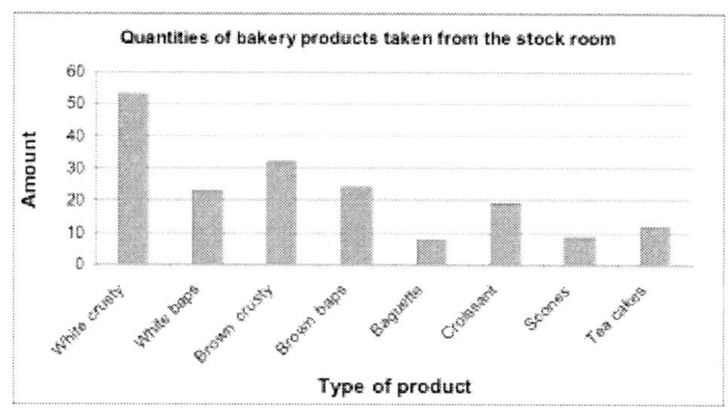

3.

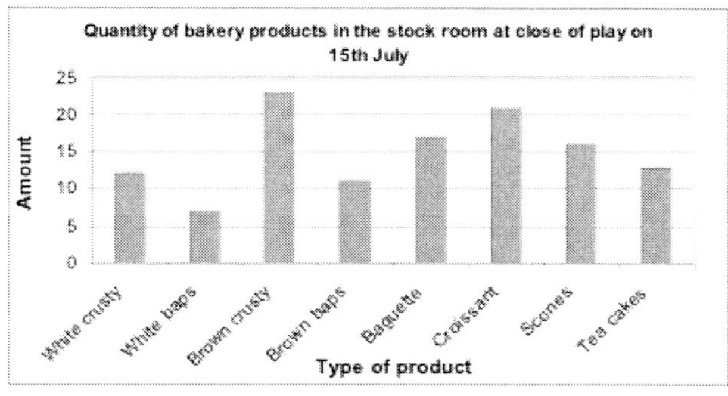

40. Factory – deliveries

1. Approximately 37 miles
2. A40 and A4076
3. Cardiff

4. Milford Haven
5. 6
6. Approximately 27 miles
7. Approximately 33 miles
8. Approximately 140 miles

41. Factory – comparing performance

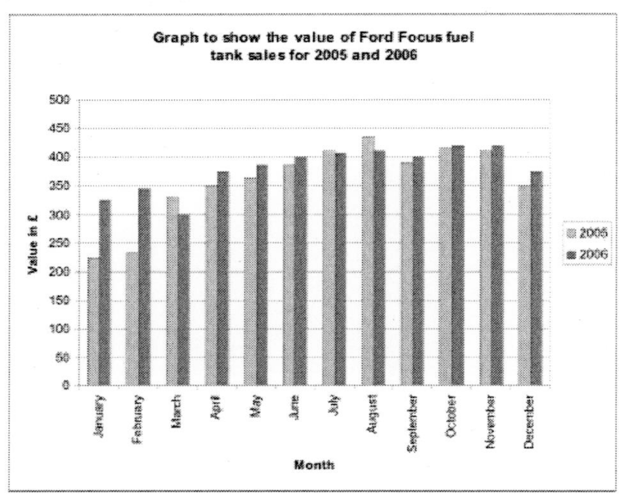

You should check your other answers with your teacher.

42. Factory – courier service

Weight	40 kg	41 kg	42 kg	43 kg	44 kg	45 kg
Tally	||||	𝍸 ||||	𝍸 𝍸	𝍸 ||||	𝍸 ||	|||
Number	4	9	10	9	7	3

1. 42
2. 19
3. 23
4.

Weight	40 kg	41 kg	42 kg	43 kg	44 kg	45 kg
Cost	£8.00	£9.50	£11.00	£12.50	£14.00	£15.50

5. £70.50

43. Factory – vending machine

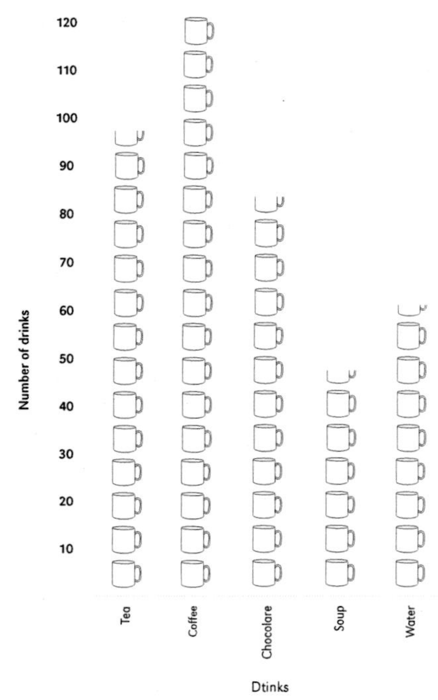

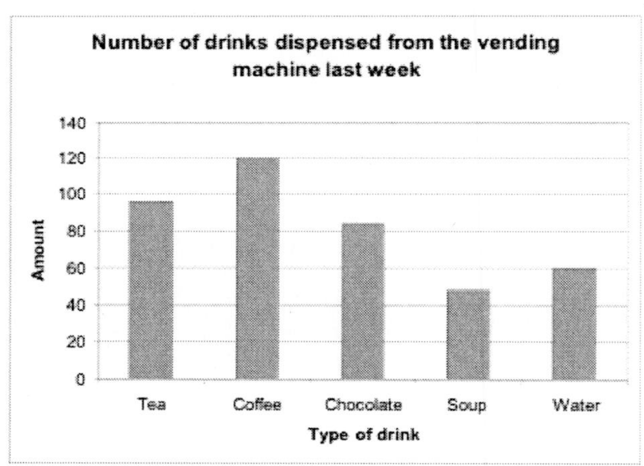

44. Factory – birthday lists

You should check your answers with your teacher.

45. Factory – fire safety training

Fire safety training		
	Activity	Time
1	Coffee and sign register	1.00 pm
2	Fire hazards	1.15 pm
3	Walk around	1.30 pm
4	Fire procedures	1.40 pm
5	Evacuation procedure	2.05 pm
6	Types of fire extinguishers	2.15 pm
7	Break	3.00 pm
8	Types of fire	3.15 pm
9	Hands-on session	3.35 pm
10	Training ends	4.00 pm
Total training time		2.5 hours

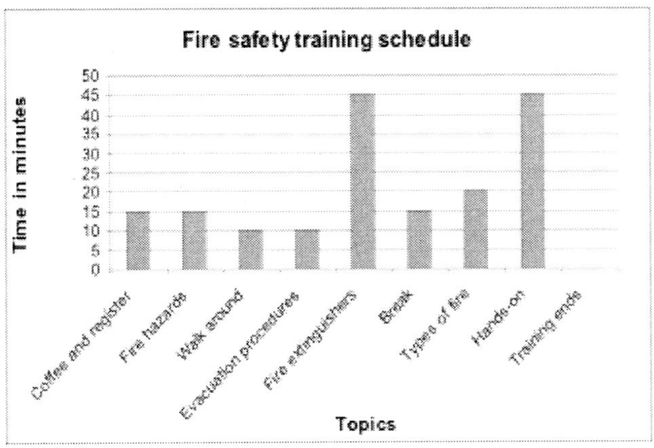

46. Factory – party buffet

	£7.95	£8.75	£9.50	£10.50
Tally	𝍸𝍸𝍸𝍸𝍸 𝍸𝍸𝍸𝍸IIII	𝍸𝍸𝍸𝍸𝍸 𝍸𝍸	𝍸𝍸𝍸𝍸𝍸 𝍸𝍸𝍸𝍸𝍸 𝍸𝍸𝍸𝍸IIII	𝍸𝍸𝍸𝍸𝍸 𝍸𝍸𝍸𝍸𝍸 𝍸𝍸III
Number	49	35	74	63
Cost	£389.55	£306.25	£703.00	£661.50

47. Factory – new uniforms

Uniform requisition form – Production lines 1–4	
Size	Quantity
XS	1
S	2
M	1
L	4
XL	2
XXL	3
XXXL	1

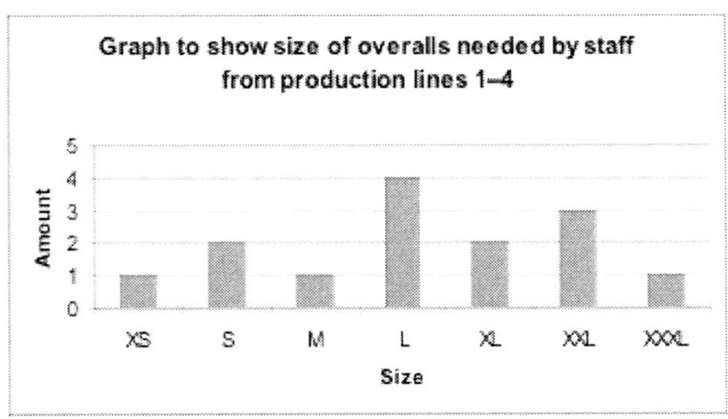

48. Factory – website

1. Tuesday, Wednesday and Thursday.
2. 10
3. 20
4. Tuesday and Thursday
5. No, she did 31 hours.

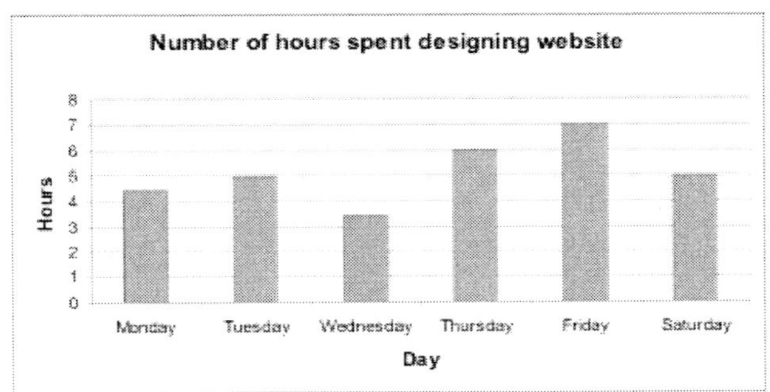

49. Factory – rates of pay

Hourly rate	Tally	Total
£5.55	𝍸𝍸𝍸	15
£6.15	𝍸𝍸𝍸𝍸𝍸III	28
£6.25	𝍸𝍸𝍸IIII	19
£6.75	𝍸𝍸	10
£7.50	𝍸𝍸𝍸𝍸𝍸𝍸𝍸𝍸II	42

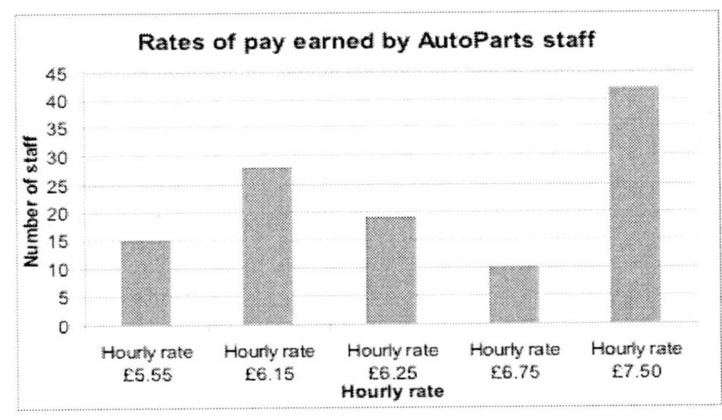

You should check the findings of your survey with your teacher.

50. Factory – milometer readings

AUTOPARTS DELIVERY				DY03TDR
Date	Driver	TACHOMETER READING		
		Out of yard	Into yard	MILEAGE
7th April	K. Patton	10273	10397	124
8th April		10397	10524	127
9th April		10524	10639	115
10th April		10639	10727	88
11th April		10727	10856	129
TOTAL				583

AUTOPARTS DELIVERY				PT03XCD
Date	Driver	TACHOMETER READING		
		Out of yard	Into yard	MILEAGE
7th April	B. Boskov	9836	9976	140
8th April		9976	10125	149
9th April		10125	10199	74
10th April		10199	10278	79
11th April		10278	10387	109
TOTAL				551

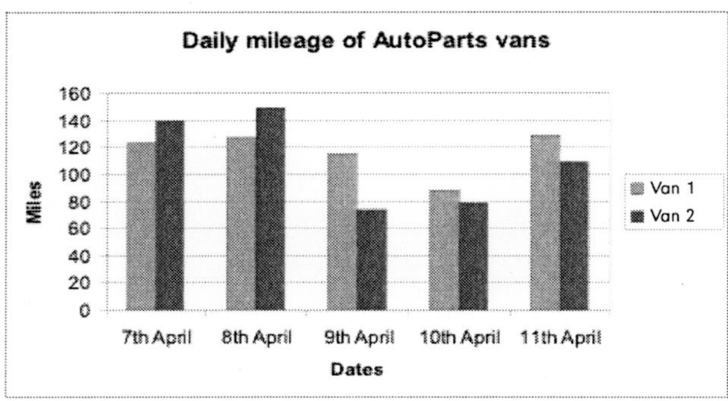

51. Factory – parking spaces

Day	Spaces
Monday	220
Tuesday	200
Wednesday	150
Thursday	230
Friday	190
Saturday	30
Sunday	10

1. Thursday
2. Sunday
3. 10 cars
4. 1030

Activity index

Handling Data entry level 3 – Curriculum elements matrix

Handling Data elements

HD1/E3 – Data and statistical measures

HD1/E3.1 – *extract numerical information from list, tables, diagrams and simple charts*

Worksheets – 1, 2, 3, 4, 5, 6, 7, 8, 9, 10, 11, 12, 13, 14, 15, 16, 17, 18, 19, 20, 21, 22, 23, 24, 25, 26, 27, 28, 29, 30, 31, 32, 33, 34, 35 36, 37, 38, 39, 40, 41, 42, 43, 44, 45, 46, 47, 48, 49, 50 and 51.

HD1/E3.2 – *make numerical comparisons from bar charts and pictograms*

Worksheets – 4, 6, 7, 8, 9, 23, 27, 29, 31, 38, 41, 48, 50 and 51.

HD1/E3.3 – *make observations and record numerical information using a tally*

Worksheets – 12, 13, 39, 42, 46 and 49.

HD1/E3.4 – *organise and represent information in different ways so that it makes sense to others*

Worksheets – 2, 3, 17, 18, 19, 20, 21, 22, 23, 25, 26, 27, 29, 30, 32, 33, 34, 35, 36, 37, 38, 39, 41, 43, 45, 46, 47, 48, 49, 50 and 51.

Number elements

N1/E2 – Whole numbers

N1/E2.2 – *read, write, order and compare numbers up to 100*

Worksheet – 35.

N1/E3 – Whole numbers

N1/E3.1 – *count, read, write, order and compare numbers up to 1000*

Worksheets – 6, 7, 8, 9, 10, 11, 12, 20, 21, 26, 30, 32, 33, 39, 42, 43, 46, 47, 48 and 50.

N1/E3.2 – *add and subtract using three-digit whole numbers*

Worksheets – 6, 7, 8, 9, 10, 11, 39 and 42.

N1/E3.4 – *Multiply two-digit whole numbers by single-digit whole numbers*

Worksheets – 8, 9 and 42.

N1/E3.6 – *divide two-digit whole numbers by single-digit whole numbers and interpret remainders*

Worksheet – 43.

N1/E3.7 – *approximate by rounding numbers less than 1000 to the nearest 10 or 100*

Worksheets – 30 and 32.

N2/E3 – Fractions, decimals and percentages

N2/E3.1 – *read, write and understand common fractions (e.g. 3/4, 2/3, 1/10)*

Worksheet – 48.

N2/E3.3 – *read, write and understand decimals up to two decimal places in practical contexts (such as: common measures to one decimal place, e.g. 1.5 m; money in decimal notation, e.g. £2.37)*

Worksheets – 26, 36, 37, 42, 46 and 49.

N2/E3.4 – *use a calculator to calculate using whole numbers and decimals to solve problems in context, and to check calculations*

Worksheets – 26, 37, 42 and 46.

Measures, shape and space elements

MSS1/E3 – Common measures

MSS1/E3.1 – *add and subtract sums of money using decimal notation*

Worksheets – 11, 37, 42 and 46.

MSS1/E3.3 – *read, measure and record time*

Worksheets – 18, 22, 24, 25, 34, 35, 44, 45 and 48.

MSS1/E3.4 – *read and interpret distance in everyday situations*

Worksheets – 16, 28 and 40.

MSS1/E3.5 – *read, estimate, measure and compare length using non-standard and standard units*

Worksheet – 5.

MSS1/E3.6 – *read, estimate, measure and compare weight using non-standard and standard units*

Worksheets – 37 and 41.

MSS1/E3.9 – *read, measure and compare temperature using common units and instruments*

Worksheets – 10 and 17.

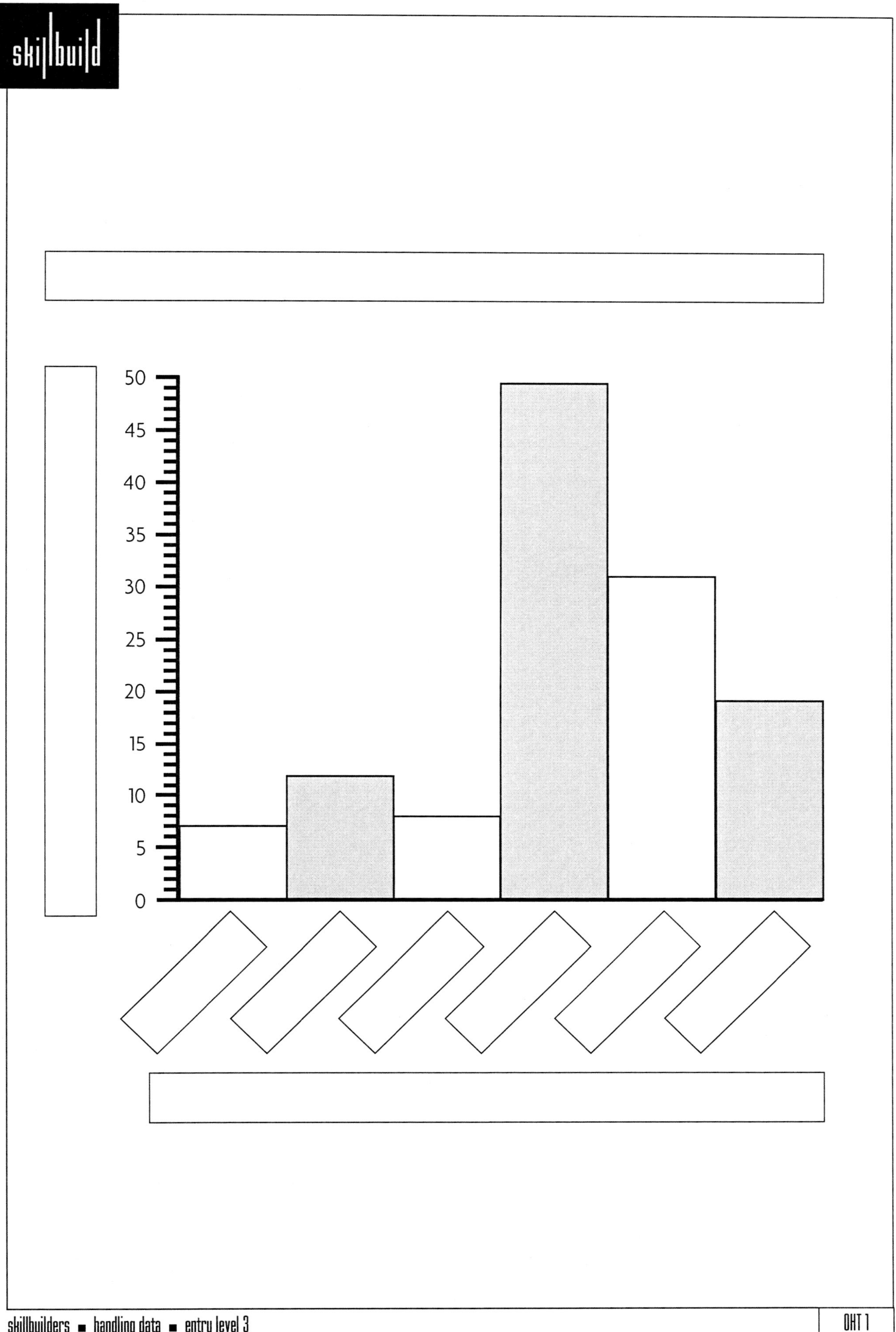
skillbuild
50
45
40
35
30
25
20
15
10
5
0

skillbuild

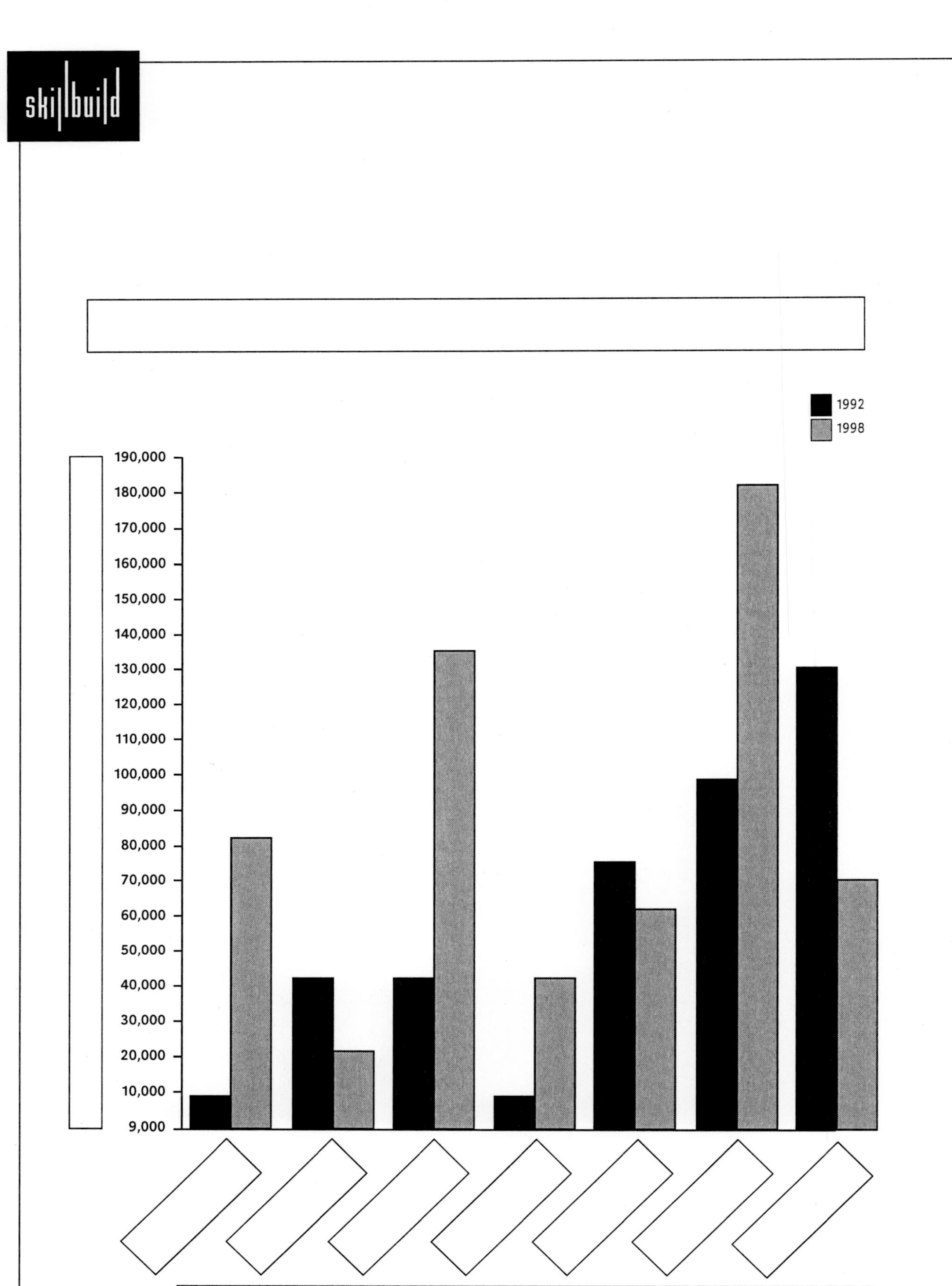

1992
1998
190,000
180,000
170,000
160,000
150,000
140,000
130,000
120,000
110,000
100,000
90,000
80,000
70,000
60,000
50,000
40,000
30,000
20,000
10,000
9,000

3 m

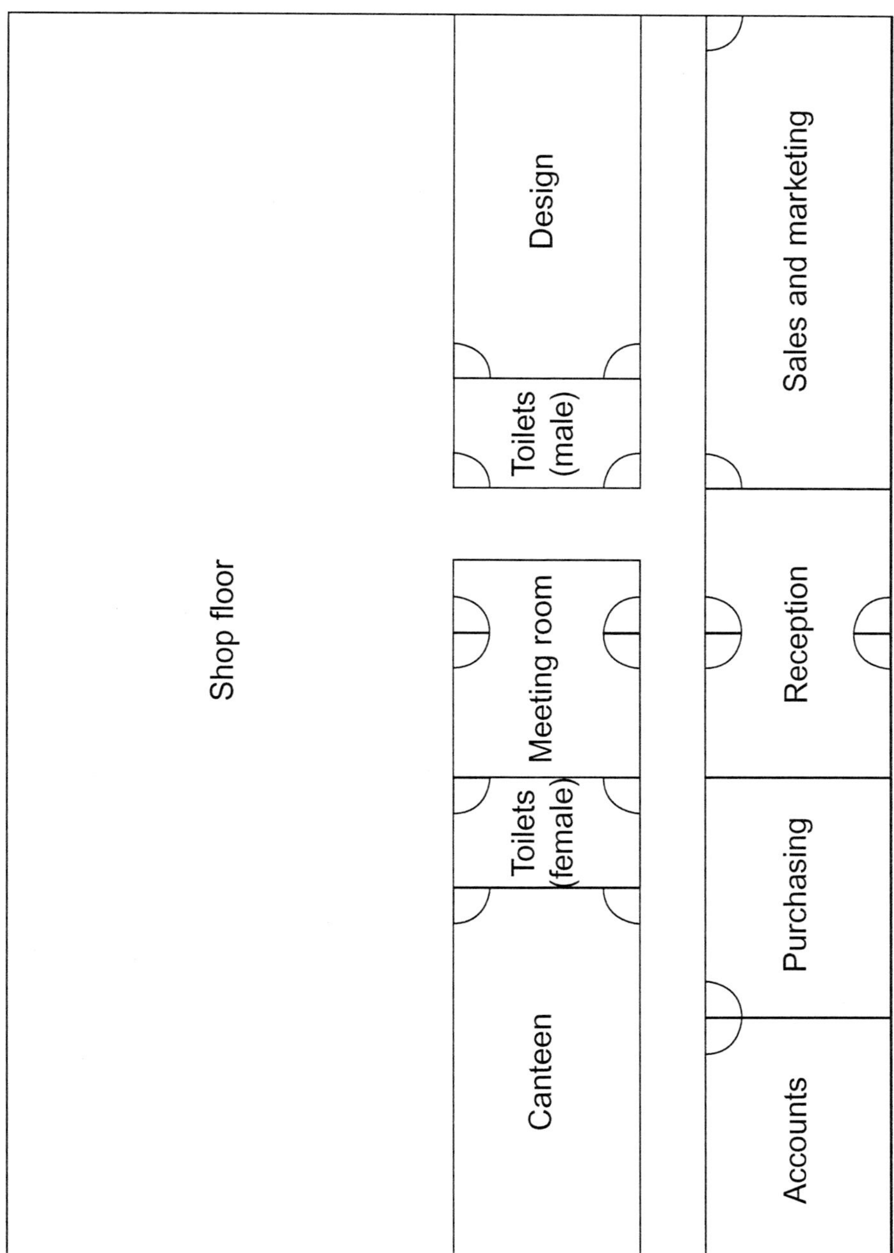
Shop floor
Design
Toilets (male)
Meeting room
Toilets (female)
Canteen
Sales and marketing
Reception
Purchasing
Accounts

skillbuild

UK imports of bananas 1992 and 1998 by principal countries

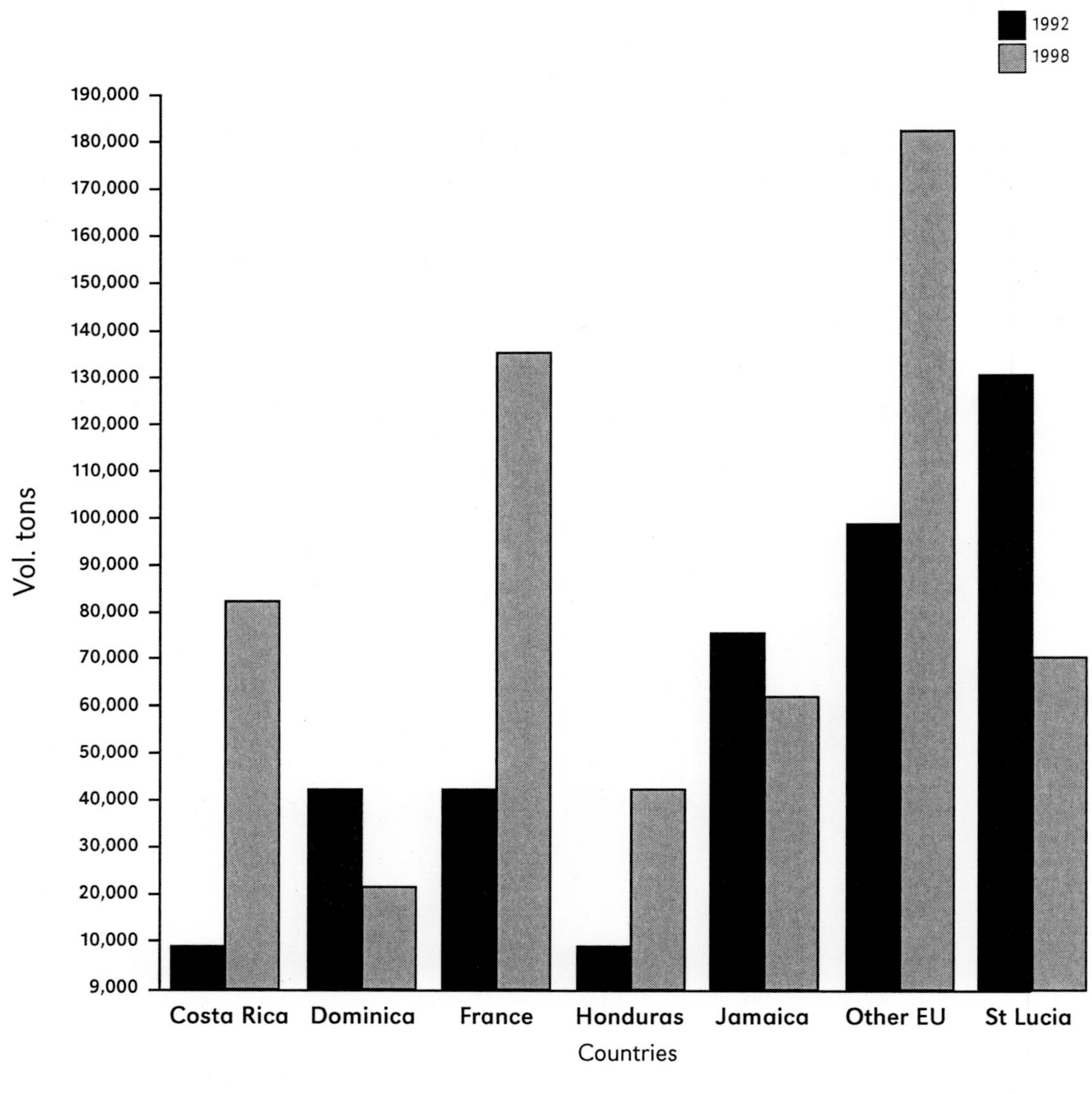

Number of drinks dispensed by vending machine in Blackwell's staffroom on Monday 14th August 2006

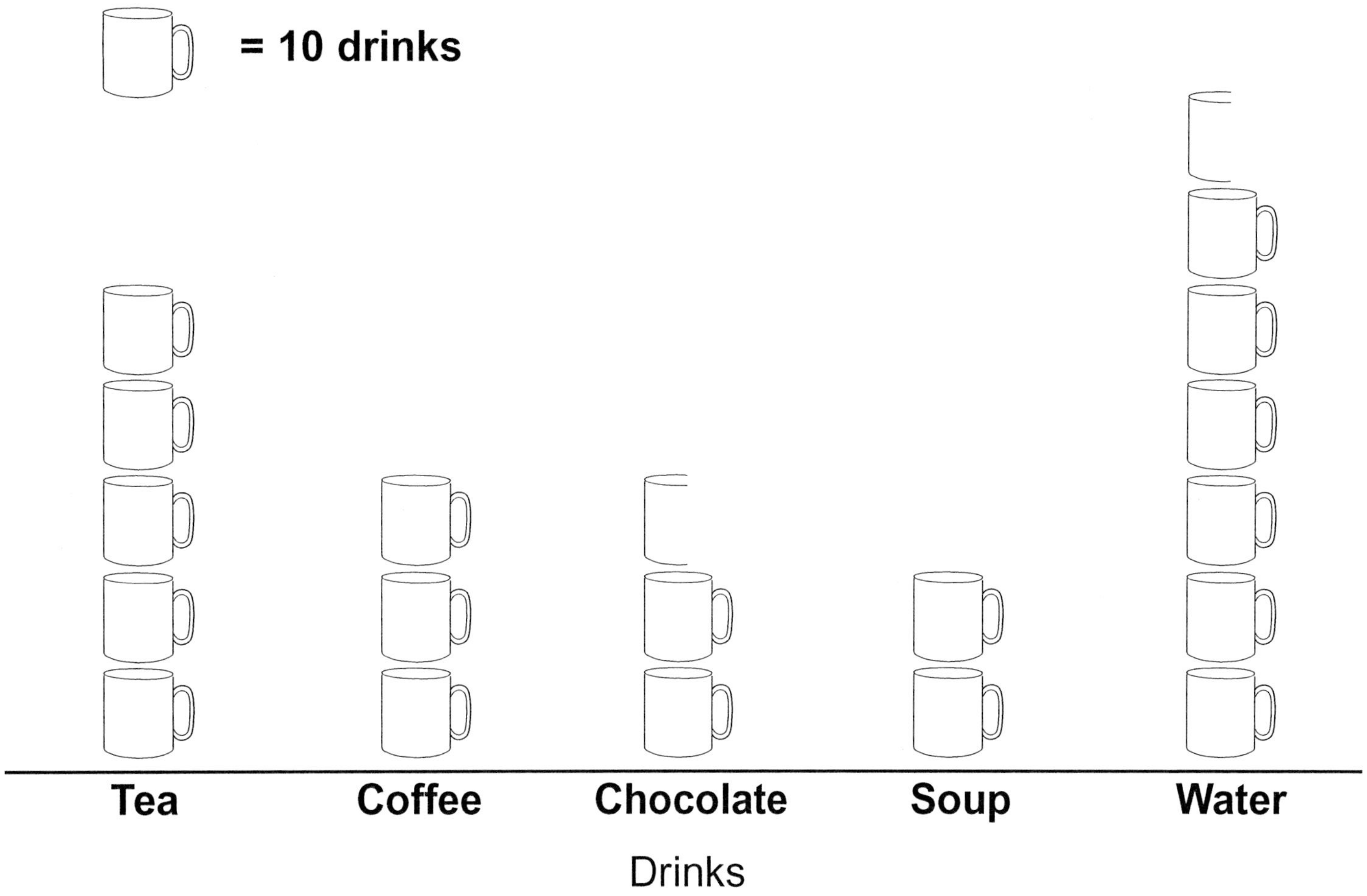

= 10 drinks

Tea **Coffee** **Chocolate** **Soup** **Water**

Drinks

Monthly sales, figures given in 100,000

	Food	Non-food	All sales
Aug. '04	6.8	6.0	6.4
Sept. '04	7.9	5.5	6.7
Oct. '04	7.6	8.1	7.9
Nov. '04	8.6	7.4	8.0
Dec. '04	6.0	10.5	8.4
Jan. '05	11.6	7.8	9.6
Feb. '05	8.3	14.1	11.3
Mar. '05	8.4	11.9	10.2
Apr. '05	4.5	3.9	4.2
May '05	3.5	5.1	4.4
June '05	5.0	8.1	6.6
July '05	5.5	4.3	4.9
Aug. '05	7.0	5.2	6.0
June-Aug. '05	5.8	6.1	6.0